M140

Introducing statistics

Book 4

# Association and estimation

This publication forms part of an Open University module. Details of this and other Open University modules can be obtained from the Student Registration and Enquiry Service, The Open University, PO Box 197, Milton Keynes MK7 6BJ, United Kingdom (tel. +44 (0)845 300 6090; email general-enquiries@open.ac.uk).

Alternatively, you may visit the Open University website at www.open.ac.uk where you can learn more about the wide range of modules and packs offered at all levels by The Open University.

To purchase a selection of Open University materials visit www.ouw.co.uk, or contact Open University Worldwide, Walton Hall, Milton Keynes MK7 6AA, United Kingdom for a brochure (tel. +44 (0)1908 858779; fax +44 (0)1908 858787; email ouw-customer-services@open.ac.uk).

The Open University, Walton Hall, Milton Keynes, MK7 6AA.

First published 2013.

Edited, designed and typeset by The Open University, using the Open University TEX System.

Printed in the United Kingdom by The Charlesworth Group, Wakefield.

ISBN 978 1 7800 7665 2

1.1

# Contents

# Contents

Unit 8

# Teaching how to read

# Introduction

For most of the data you have met in previous units, the numbers in the dataset have had an intrinsic meaning. For example, the miles per gallon that a particular car achieved (Unit 1, Section 3), the price of a jar of coffee (Unit 2, Section 1) or the gross hourly earnings of men and women (Unit 3, Section 1). Some of the statistical techniques you have already learned about, such as the $z$-tests in Unit 7, are appropriate for such data. In contrast, Unit 8 focuses on data where numbers are used only as labels (or not used at all) – and on statistical methods specifically designed for such data.

The theme of this unit is learning how to read and, more particularly, which teaching methods produce the best results. Section 1 provides some background, clarifies the questions of interest, and describes a large study to investigate different methods of teaching how to read. The data from the study are in *categorical form*, where the categories are determined, for example, by the teaching method used, or whether a given standard has been met or not. The data are presented in tables of a particular type, called *contingency tables*.

Section 2 describes how contingency tables are constructed, and how they are used to study relationships between variables. In Section 3, you will learn more about probabilities of various kinds, and how they are related. Then in Section 4 a hypothesis test known as the $\chi^2$ *test for contingency tables* is introduced. This follows a similar procedure to that in the previous two units. We set up null and alternative hypotheses and then calculate a test statistic. We then compare the test statistic with critical values at the 5% and 1% significance levels and so decide whether or not to reject the null hypothesis. Section 5 makes further use of this test, with particular reference to the ideas of association and causality in assessing the impact of teaching methods on literacy; it also discusses some reservations about the conclusions from a large study investigating methods for teaching how to read, and about conclusions from hypothesis tests in general. Finally, Section 6 directs you to the Computer Book which describes how to use Minitab to analyse data in the form of contingency tables.

The symbol $\chi$ is the Greek letter chi, pronounced *ki* (to rhyme with tie); $\chi^2$ is pronounced *ki squared*.

# 1 The best way of teaching how to read

Reading is a key skill that children are expected to master early in their schooling. So an important question for educators, and the question that forms the theme for this unit, is:

*What is the best way of teaching how to read?*

In this unit, you will mainly consider data from one study designed to help answer this question. In Subsection 1.2, the question will be clarified, and in Subsection 1.3 the study itself will be described. However, first Subsection 1.1 provides some background.

## 1.1 The 'reading wars'

Unlike languages such as Spanish, Finnish and Swahili, where there is a direct correspondence between how words sound and how they are written, English spelling is far from transparent – for example, the 'o' is pronounced differently in 'grove', 'move' and 'top', while the spelling of words like 'bomb', 'knot', 'enough' and 'aisle' defies logic. This feature of the English language has generated much debate about how best to teach reading at primary school and in particular what emphasis to place on relating the letters of the alphabet to the individual sounds that words are made up of.

## Phonemes and graphemes

A **phoneme** is a term used to describe an individual sound that can distinguish one word from another.

A **grapheme** is a term used to describe a letter, or combination of letters, of the alphabet corresponding to an individual sound.

For example, the word 'cat' comprises three phonemes corresponding to the sounds associated with the three graphemes (individual letters in this case) 'c', 'a' and 't'.

Choosing which teaching method to use has been very controversial, giving rise to what has been called the 'reading wars'. Several reviews have established that it is important for children to be able to use grapheme–phoneme, or letter–sound, correspondences, also known as **phonics**. Thus teaching methods based solely on learning whole words have largely been superseded by methods that involve teaching phonics.

However, there are several teaching approaches that involve phonics, and so the debate continues. One is a 'top-down' approach in which children are taught to recognise whole words before *analysing* how they can be broken down into grapheme–phoneme correspondences. This approach, which is called **analytic phonics**, was widely used in Britain until relatively recently. A contrasting approach is to start with intensive teaching of how letters of the alphabet relate to phonemes, and building these up – *synthesizing* them – into whole words. This approach is called **synthetic phonics**, and has recently been introduced in many schools across Britain.

## Here is Peter, here is Jane

If you learned how to read in Britain in the 1960s, the chances are that you will have met Peter and Jane, the main characters of the books published by Ladybird as part of the Key Words Reading Scheme (Figure 1). This teaching method, also known as 'Look and Say', was based entirely on learning whole words. Using a limited vocabulary with much repetition – resulting in stilted prose and very odd-sounding conversations – the aim was to teach children to recognise the most commonly used words.

**Figure 1** The first of the Peter and Jane series, published in 1964

## 1.2  Clarifying the question

Subsection 1.3 will describe a large study that was conducted in order to decide which method is most effective for teaching how to read. We will keep returning to this study throughout the unit. However, the question *What is the best way of teaching how to read?* is a very general one, and so needs to be clarified before it can be addressed.

**Activity 1**  *Clarifying a question*

1. Clarify

Briefly think about the question *What is the best way of teaching how to read?*, and write down two or three of its key aspects which *you* think need to be clarified. (The wording of the question is a useful guide.)

In Subsection 1.1, two contrasting methods for teaching how to read at school were described: analytic phonics and synthetic phonics. Thus it would seem natural to design a study to compare these two distinct approaches.

Reading ability comprises many facets, which cannot easily be reduced to a single measurement: thus several aspects of reading ability ought to be evaluated. One standardised single-word reading test, called the British Ability Scales Word Reading Test, or BAS test for short, provides a standardised reading score. This test enables the reading ability of a child aged under 14.5 years old to be classified according to whether or not the child's reading age is above their chronological age (so the test tells you whether or not a child is reading well for their age). Other tests may be used to assess reading comprehension, spelling ability, and other aspects of reading skill.

The effectiveness of a method for teaching how to read can be judged by the proportion of children whose reading age is higher than their chronological age, as measured by the BAS test, for example. The BAS test was also used as a measure of reading ability in Unit 7, where results from the British Cohort Study were examined.

## 1.3   The Clackmannanshire study

The data in this unit come from an influential study undertaken by Rhona Johnston and Joyce Watson over seven years in several schools in Clackmannanshire (Figure 2) involving some 300 children in 13 classes. (Johnston and Watson (2004) 'Accelerating the development of reading, spelling and phonemic awareness skills in initial readers', *Reading and Writing: An Interdisciplinary Journal*, vol. 17, pp. 327–357.) This study compared three methods for teaching how to read in the first year of primary school. Two of the methods were analytic phonics and synthetic phonics, which were described in Subsection 1.1. In addition, a third teaching method was evaluated, which combined analytic phonics with training in phonological awareness (the ability to recognise the different sounds of which spoken words are made up). This method will be referred to as analytic phonics + PA. Eleven different aspects of reading ability were evaluated for each child, including the BAS reading test described in Subsection 1.2.

Clearly, teaching methods are applied to whole classes, rather than to individual children. Some care in selecting the participating classes and schools was needed to ensure that the children within the three different groups (taught using analytic phonics, taught using synthetic phonics and taught using analytic phonics + PA) were broadly comparable and that any imbalances were known about in advance.

**Figure 2**   Clackmannanshire, at the heart of Scotland

2. Collect

---

**Example 1**   *Comparability across the groups*

All the children within the selected classes were 5-year-old new school entrants, whose first language was English. Socio-economic background may influence reading ability, so information on such factors was obtained. In Clackmannanshire, schools are classified according to an index of disadvantage ranging from −1 (least deprived) to 2.5 (most deprived). The analytic phonics group scored −0.13 on this index, whereas the analytic phonics + PA group scored 0.05, and the synthetic phonics group 1.12. Thus, the children in the synthetic phonics group came from slightly more disadvantaged socio-economic backgrounds than children from the other groups.

---

**Activity 2**   *Making comparisons at baseline*

In Example 1, some differences in socio-economic background between the groups were described. There may well be other factors that might have influenced reading ability even before formal teaching began. Such differences between groups at the start of the study ('at baseline') would mean that we were not comparing like with like.

Briefly suggest how to check that, at the start of the study, the children have comparable reading ability.

In the Clackmannanshire study, the children were tested two weeks after starting school, but before the teaching of reading started. Then the three teaching programmes were introduced, lasting 16 school weeks, after which the children were tested again. Further testing took place subsequently, to monitor the children's progress.

## Exercise on Section 1

### Exercise 1    *Investigating differences between girls and boys*

There is some evidence to suggest that boys and girls learn how to read differently, and may thus respond differently to different teaching methods. Briefly outline how such effects might be investigated.

"It's called 'reading'. It's how people install new software into their brains"

# 2 Contingency tables

In the Clackmannanshire study described in Subsection 1.3, each child was classified according to whether their reading age (as measured by the BAS reading test) was higher than their chronological age (that is, 'better than expected for their age'), or whether it was less than or equal to their chronological age. This gives rise to a table of counts called a *contingency table*.

## 2.1   Tables and proportions

**Example 2**   *The baseline test results*

The results of the baseline test in the Clackmannanshire study (prior to starting the teaching programme) are shown in Table 1.

**Table 1**   Results from the baseline test

| | Reading age as compared to chronological age | |
| --- | --- | --- |
| | Not higher | Higher |
| Analytic phonics | 69 | 39 |
| Analytic phonics + PA | 43 | 35 |
| Synthetic phonics | 76 | 41 |

The three rows of numbers in the table correspond to the three groups, and the two columns of numbers correspond to reading ability, classified as reading age less than or equal to, or higher than, chronological age. The numbers in the table are numbers of children. So, for example, 69 children in the analytic phonics group had a reading age which was equal to or less than their chronological age.

One question of interest, for the baseline test data, is to check that any differences between the groups are small. (We would expect to see some differences, owing to random fluctuations.) You learned a way to quantify such differences in Unit 6 using probabilities; this is the topic of Example 3.

3. Analyse

**Example 3** *Calculating probabilities from the baseline test results*

To calculate probabilities, it's convenient to have the totals available, for both the rows and the columns. These totals, which are called **marginal totals**, are shown in Table 2 (which will be referred to at various points in the unit).

**Table 2** Results from the baseline test, with marginal totals

| | Reading age as compared to chronological age | | |
|---|---|---|---|
| | Not higher | Higher | Total |
| Analytic phonics | 69 | 39 | 108 |
| Analytic phonics + PA | 43 | 35 | 78 |
| Synthetic phonics | 76 | 41 | 117 |
| Total | 188 | 115 | 303 |

We obtain probabilities from a contingency table by calculating *proportions*. For example, if a child in the analytic phonics (AP) group is selected at random, then the probability that a child's reading age is higher than their chronological age is:

$$\frac{\text{number in AP group with reading age} > \text{chronological age}}{\text{number in AP group}}$$

$$= \frac{39}{108} \simeq 0.361.$$

Multiplying this result by 100 gives about 36.1%.

Also of interest is the overall proportion of children who could read well for their age, before beginning to learn how to read at school. This can be calculated using the column totals. So the probability a child in the study has reading age above their chronological age is:

$$\frac{\text{total number with reading age} > \text{chronological age}}{\text{total number in study}}$$

$$= \frac{115}{303} \simeq 0.380.$$

Multiplying this result by 100 gives about 38.0%.

**Activity 3** *Comparing proportions at baseline*

Use the data in Table 2 to do the following.

(a) Obtain the percentage of children in the analytic phonics + PA group whose reading age is higher than their chronological age. Do the same for children in the synthetic phonics group.

(b) Compare these proportions informally. What do you conclude about the comparability of the three groups?

In Activity 3 you found some moderate differences between groups in the baseline test; this is not unexpected, as some differences will arise from random fluctuations. The question is whether the differences that were observed could plausibly have arisen due to chance. This topic will be addressed in Section 4.

As previously mentioned, the children were tested again after 16 school weeks of teaching. The results are given in Example 4, and discussed in Activity 4.

Learning how to read

**Example 4** *The first follow-up test results*

Table 3 shows the contingency table of results on the BAS reading test at the first follow-up test for the Clackmannanshire study after 16 school weeks. (Table 3 will be referred to at various points in the unit.)

**Table 3** Results from the first follow-up test

| | Reading age as compared to chronological age | | |
| --- | --- | --- | --- |
| | Not higher | Higher | Total |
| Analytic phonics | 68 | 36 | 104 |
| Analytic phonics + PA | 51 | 24 | 75 |
| Synthetic phonics | 35 | 78 | 113 |
| Total | 154 | 138 | 292 |

Note that the total numbers in each group have dropped a little, perhaps because some children changed schools or moved out of the area. The biggest change, however, is in the numbers of children performing well in the synthetic phonics group.

**Activity 4** *Comparing proportions at first follow-up*

Use the data in Table 3 to do the following.

(a) Obtain the percentages of children in the three groups whose reading age at the first follow-up test is greater than their chronological age.

(b) Compare these percentages informally.

(c) What further information might you require to interpret these results?

Activity 4 suggests that, for reading ability as measured by the BAS reading test, synthetic phonics is a more effective teaching method than analytic phonics or analytic phonics supplemented with phonological awareness training. However, as indicated after Activity 3, a more formal hypothesis test is required to interpret such data.

Contingency tables are an effective way of displaying such data, and statistical methods have been developed to analyse them. You will encounter some of these methods in this unit. (Note that the published analysis of the Clackmannanshire study used more complex methods. However, the conclusions are the same as those that will be made in this unit.)

## 2.2  Identifying contingency tables

We have now introduced some of the data, in the form of contingency tables, to help us investigate the question clarified in Subsection 1.2: *What is the best way of teaching how to read?* In this subsection we shall look more closely at the form of the data presented in Tables 2 and 3 in Subsection 2.1. For ease of reference, Table 3 is reproduced here.

**Table 4**   Results from the first follow-up test (reproduced from Table 3)

|  | Reading age as compared to chronological age | | |
|---|---|---|---|
|  | Not higher | Higher | Total |
| Analytic phonics | 68 | 36 | 104 |
| Analytic phonics + PA | 51 | 24 | 75 |
| Synthetic phonics | 35 | 78 | 113 |
| Total | 154 | 138 | 292 |

In this table, each child in the sample of 292 children is assigned to one of three teaching method categories, and to one of two reading age categories. The teaching method and reading age variables are described as **categorical** variables, as they are each made up of a certain number of categories; each child can be classified into one of these categories. In particular, we are not told the children's actual scores on the BAS reading test, or their reading ages, so the data are of a different form from the data that we used when we applied the $z$-test in Unit 7.

In Table 4, the categories for each of the variables are mutually exclusive. (You met this expression in Unit 6 (Subsection 2.2) when discussing probabilities of events and the addition rule.) This means that each child can belong to one and only one category on each variable.

### Contingency tables

A contingency table is a table which meets the following three conditions:

* the row variable and the column variable are both *categorical*
* the categories for both variables are *mutually exclusive*
* the entry in each cell of the table is a *count*.

**Example 5**  *Contingency table or not?*

In Activity 4 (Subsection 2.1) you obtained the percentages of children in each teaching group whose reading age at the first follow-up test was higher than their chronological age. These percentages, together with those of children with reading age not higher than chronological age, are shown in Table 5.

**Table 5**   First follow-up test: percentages with reading age higher/not higher than chronological age

|  | Reading age as compared to chronological age | |
|  | Not higher (%) | Higher (%) |
|---|---|---|
| Analytic phonics | 65.4 | 34.6 |
| Analytic phonics + PA | 68.0 | 32.0 |
| Synthetic phonics | 31.0 | 69.0 |

Children reading ... or just looking at the pictures?

The variables displayed in Table 5 are categorical, and the categories are mutually exclusive. However, the entries are percentages, not counts. Hence this table is *not* a contingency table.

Table 6 provides a little more insight into how many children progressed between tests. (In this table we have replaced 'Not higher' by 'Low' and 'Higher' by 'High' to shorten the column headings.)

**Table 6**   Reading ability at baseline and at first follow-up test

|  | Reading ages at baseline/follow-up | | | | |
|  | Low/Low | Low/High | High/Low | High/High | Total |
|---|---|---|---|---|---|
| Analytic phonics | 50 | 16 | 17 | 20 | 103 |
| Analytic phonics + PA | 30 | 10 | 21 | 14 | 75 |
| Synthetic phonics | 23 | 52 | 12 | 26 | 113 |
| Total | 103 | 78 | 50 | 60 | 291 |

Thus, for example, in the analytic phonics group, 50 children scored Low on both tests, 16 scored Low on the baseline test and High on the first follow-up test, 17 scored High on the baseline test and Low on the first follow-up test, and 20 scored High on both tests. Note that the baseline values are missing for one child, so the total is 291 rather than 292 as in Table 4.

Is this table a contingency table? The variables are certainly categorical, and the categories are mutually exclusive, since each child can only be in one of the four cells Low/Low, Low/High, High/Low, High/High. And finally, the entries are counts. So yes, this is a contingency table.

Recognising contingency tables is important, because the statistical test described in Section 4 applies *only* to contingency tables. Activity 5 will give you some more practice at identifying which tables are contingency tables and which are not.

**Activity 5    *Identifying contingency tables***

Say whether the following tables are contingency tables, stating reasons why or why not.

(a) Table 7 gives the average ages of the children in the three teaching groups at baseline test and at first follow-up test.

**Table 7**    Average chronological age of children at baseline and first follow-up tests

|  | Chronological age at test (years) | |
|---|---|---|
|  | Baseline test | First follow-up test |
| Analytic phonics | 5.01 | 5.43 |
| Analytic phonics + PA | 5.01 | 5.41 |
| Synthetic phonics | 5.00 | 5.48 |

(b) Table 8 shows the numbers of children (among those who did the follow-up test) whose reading age was higher than their chronological age at the baseline and at the first follow-up tests. (Note: this table was derived from Table 6.)

**Table 8**    Reading ability at baseline and at first follow-up test

|  | Standardised reading age at baseline and first follow-up | |
|---|---|---|
|  | High at baseline | High at first follow-up |
| Analytic phonics | 37 | 36 |
| Analytic phonics + PA | 35 | 24 |
| Synthetic phonics | 38 | 78 |

A contingency table is usually described in terms of the number of categories of each variable. For example, in Table 4, the *teaching method* variable has three categories, and the *reading ability* variable has two categories. This table is therefore said to be a

$3 \times 2$ contingency table (where '$3 \times 2$' is read as 'three by two').

In general, if the variable corresponding to the rows has $r$ categories and the variable corresponding to the columns has $c$ categories, the contingency table is described as an **$r \times c$ contingency table**. It may also be said to be of **size $r \times c$**, or of **dimension $r \times c$**.

**Activity 6** *Determining sizes of contingency tables*

(a) Write down the dimension of Table 6 from Example 5.

(b) Suppose that rows and columns were swapped around in Table 4. What would be the dimension of the swapped-round version of the table?

## Exercises on Section 2

**Exercise 2** *Examining a gender distribution*

Table 9 shows the gender distribution by teaching group in the Clackmannanshire study.

**Table 9**  Gender distribution by teaching group

|  | Gender | | |
|---|---|---|---|
|  | Boys | Girls | Total |
| Analytic phonics | 58 | 51 | 109 |
| Analytic phonics + PA | 39 | 39 | 78 |
| Synthetic phonics | 61 | 56 | 117 |
| Total | 158 | 146 | 304 |

(a) Obtain the percentage of girls in the study as a whole, to one decimal place.

(b) Obtain the proportions of boys in each teaching group.

(c) Comment briefly (and informally) on any differences you observe between groups.

**Exercise 3**   *Contingency or not contingency?*

Tables 10 and 11 below were both derived from Table 9. In Table 10, the category 'analytic phonics with or without PA' is obtained by combining the categories 'analytic phonics' and 'analytic phonics + PA' from Table 9.

**Table 10**   Gender distribution by teaching group

|  | Gender | | |
|---|---|---|---|
|  | Boys | Girls | Total |
| Analytic phonics with or without PA | 97 | 90 | 187 |
| Synthetic phonics | 61 | 56 | 117 |
| Total | 158 | 146 | 304 |

**Table 11**   Gender distribution by teaching group (%)

|  | Gender | |
|---|---|---|
|  | Boys | Girls |
| Analytic phonics | 53 | 47 |
| Analytic phonics + PA | 50 | 50 |
| Synthetic phonics | 52 | 48 |

(a) For each table, say whether it is a contingency table, giving reasons for your answer.

(b) Write down the dimension of each of the contingency table(s) you identified in part (a).

# 3   Calculating probabilities

'To us, probability is the very guide of life' – attributed to Cicero (106–43 BC).

In this section, you will learn more about calculating probabilities, following on from the material in Unit 6. However, first the next phase of the Clackmannanshire study is described.

**Example 6**   *The second follow-up test*

At the first follow-up test, as suggested in Example 4 (Subsection 2.1), it became apparent that children in the synthetic phonics group were progressing much more rapidly than those in the other two teaching groups. For ethical reasons, it would be unacceptable to withhold a more effective teaching programme. Thus, from then on, all children were taught using the synthetic phonics method. At the end of the following school year, all the children were retested once more. The results of this second follow-up test, using the BAS reading score as before, are shown in Table 12; the row variable now describes the teaching group to which the children were originally allocated.

A bust of Cicero

**Table 12**   Results from the second follow-up test

| | Reading age as compared to chronological age | | |
| | Not higher | Higher | Total |
|---|---|---|---|
| Analytic phonics | 19 | 78 | 97 |
| Analytic phonics + PA | 11 | 55 | 66 |
| Synthetic phonics | 15 | 90 | 105 |
| Total | 45 | 223 | 268 |

It appears from Table 12 (which will be referred to at various points in the unit) that the three teaching groups are much more similar at the second follow-up test than they were at the first follow-up test. Thus the proportion of children initially allocated to the analytic phonics group whose reading age is higher than their chronological age is

$$\frac{78}{97} \simeq 0.804,$$

while it is

$$\frac{55}{66} \simeq 0.833$$

for children initially allocated to the analytic phonics + PA group, and

$$\frac{90}{105} \simeq 0.857$$

for children initially allocated to the synthetic phonics group.

Thus the children in the two analytic phonics groups appear to have 'caught up' with their peers in the synthetic phonics group, following the decision to include all children in the synthetic phonics programme.

At this point we shall pause the teaching story, and consider in a little more detail different types of probabilities (proportions), including those calculated informally in Example 6.

## 3.1   Joint and conditional probabilities

In this subsection, we shall make an important distinction between probabilities involving two events $A$ and $B$.

The **joint probability of $A$ and $B$**, denoted $P(A \text{ and } B)$, is the probability that both $A$ and $B$ occur together. In contrast, the **conditional probability of $A$ given $B$**, denoted $P(A|B)$, is the probability that $A$ occurs given that $B$ occurs. Note that we do not require $A$ and $B$ to be mutually exclusive in these definitions.

Example 7 shows how these definitions work for the data from the second follow-up test of the Clackmannanshire study.

**Example 7**   *Joint and conditional probabilities at the second follow-up*

In order to avoid cumbersome descriptions, let us first label events as follows.

- Event $R_2$: reading age higher than chronological age at the second follow-up test.

  (Similarly, $R_0$ and $R_1$ will refer to reading age being higher than chronological age at the baseline and first follow-up tests, respectively.)

- Event $AP$: initially allocated to the analytic phonics group.

- Event $AP+$: initially allocated to the analytic phonics + PA group.

- Event $SP$: initially allocated to the synthetic phonics group.

Suppose we want the probability that a child in the study was in the $AP$ group *and* had a high reading age. That is, we wish to estimate the joint probability of events $R_2$ and $AP$ for a child chosen randomly from the study. Using the approach described in Unit 6 and applying it to the data from Table 12, this is:

$$P(R_2 \text{ and } AP) = \frac{\text{number of children with event } R_2 \text{ and event } AP}{\text{total number of children}}$$
$$= \frac{78}{268} \simeq 0.291,$$

or about 29.1%.

Now instead suppose we list all the children in the $AP$ group and randomly choose a child from this list. The probability that the chosen child experienced event $R_2$ is the conditional probability that a randomly chosen child experiences event $R_2$, given that the child experiences event $AP$. More succinctly, it is the conditional probability of event $R_2$, given event $AP$. The only children entering into the calculation are those who have experienced event $AP$. Hence,

$$P(R_2|AP) = \frac{\text{number of children experiencing } R_2 \text{ and } AP}{\text{number of children experiencing } AP}$$
$$= \frac{78}{97} \simeq 0.804,$$

or about 80.4%.

Note that $P(R_2 \text{ and } AP)$ and $P(R_2|AP)$ have the same numerator, but different denominators: for the conditional probability, the denominator is restricted to children experiencing event $AP$.

Usually, for any two events $A$ and $B$, $P(A|B)$ is not equal to $P(B|A)$. To demonstrate this, we calculate the conditional probability $P(AP|R_2)$ when we restrict our attention to those children who have a high reading age, pick one of them at random, and want the probability that the chosen child is from the $AP$ group. So now the only children entering into the calculation are those who have experienced $R_2$:

$$P(AP|R_2) = \frac{\text{number of children experiencing } AP \text{ and } R_2}{\text{number of children experiencing } R_2}$$

$$= \frac{78}{223} \simeq 0.350,$$

or about 35.0%. This is very different to $P(R_2|AP)$.

Activity 7 will give you some practice at working out joint and conditional probabilities.

## Activity 7    *Calculating joint and conditional probabilities*

Use the data in Table 12 (Section 3) to calculate the following probabilities. The event labels are as in Example 7.

(a) $P(R_2 \text{ and } SP)$.

(b) $P(R_2|SP)$.

(c) $P(AP+|R_2)$.

The notation $P(A \text{ and } B)$ and $P(A|B)$ makes it explicit whether we are referring to a joint probability or a conditional probability. When probabilities are described in words, however, care is needed to make sure you have correctly identified what type of probability is involved. This is the topic of Activity 8.

## Activity 8    *Identifying joint and conditional probabilities*

The following phrases describe probabilities involving the events $R_2$ and $SP$ described in Example 7. In each case, write down whether the probability is $P(R_2 \text{ and } SP)$, $P(R_2|SP)$, or $P(SP|R_2)$.

(a) The probability that a randomly selected child who was initially allocated to the synthetic phonics group has a reading age higher than their chronological age at the second test.

(b) The probability that a randomly selected child was initially allocated to the synthetic phonics group and has a reading age higher than their chronological age at the second test.

(c) The probability that a randomly selected child whose reading age is higher than their chronological age at the second test was initially allocated to the synthetic phonics group.

(d) The probability that a randomly selected child has a reading age higher than their chronological age at the second test and was initially allocated to the synthetic phonics group.

'I know I'm having trouble reading at a 3rd
grade level...that's why, when I grow up, I'm
going to be a 2nd grade teacher.'

In Unit 6 (Subsection 2.3), you learned the multiplication rule for
probabilities of statistically independent events: if events $A$ and $B$ are
statistically independent, then

$$P(A \text{ and } B) = P(A) \times P(B).$$

The 'and' linkage leads to the *multiplication* of probabilities. A more
general version of this rule can now be given, which applies also to pairs of
events that are *not* statistically independent. The generalisation involves
conditional probabilities.

Consider again the joint probability of events $R_2$ and $AP$, considered in
Example 7. This may be written

$$P(R_2 \text{ and } AP) = \frac{\text{number of children with event } AP \text{ and event } R_2}{\text{total number of children}}$$

$$= \frac{\text{number of children with } AP}{\text{total number of children}}$$

$$\times \frac{\text{number of children with event } R_2 \text{ and event } AP}{\text{number of children with } AP},$$

because the terms 'number of children with $AP$' cancel out top and
bottom. Notice that we have

$$P(AP) = \frac{\text{number of children with } AP}{\text{total number of children}}$$

and

$$P(R_2|AP) = \frac{\text{number of children with event } R_2 \text{ and event } AP}{\text{number of children with } AP}.$$

So, substituting these expressions into the first equation, we have

$$P(R_2 \text{ and } AP) = P(AP) \times P(R_2|AP).$$

This result can be reached in other ways. For instance, suppose a randomly chosen child is to experience both $AP$ and $R_2$. Then:

1.  The child must be in the $AP$ group, which happens with probability $P(AP)$.
2.  This child from the $AP$ group must experience $R_2$, which happens with probability $P(R_2|AP)$.

The probability that both 1 *and* 2 happen is $P(AP) \times P(R_2|AP)$, in keeping with multiplication being appropriate for the 'and' linkage.

More generally, for any two events $A$ and $B$,

$$P(A \text{ and } B) = P(B) \times P(A|B).$$

Note also that exactly the same argument yields

$$P(A \text{ and } B) = P(A) \times P(B|A),$$

since

$$P(A \text{ and } B) = P(B \text{ and } A).$$

These facts about joint and conditional probabilities are summarised in the following box.

> **Joint and conditional probabilities**
>
> Let $A$ and $B$ be any two events. The joint probability of $A$ and $B$, denoted $P(A \text{ and } B)$, is the probability that both $A$ and $B$ occur.
>
> The conditional probability of $A$ given $B$, denoted $P(A|B)$, is the probability that $A$ occurs, given that $B$ occurs.
>
> Joint and conditional probabilities are linked by the following relationships:
>
> $$P(A \text{ and } B) = P(A) \times P(B|A) = P(B) \times P(A|B).$$

Example 8 illustrates how these relationships work out on real data. For a change, we shall look at data other than reading data: this time, the data relate to spelling age, rather than reading age.

In the Clackmannanshire study, spelling age was measured using the Schonell Spelling Test, which, like the BAS reading test, is standardised to chronological age. As with the reading test, the spelling test was applied at baseline, prior to starting teaching. Then a first follow-up test was applied after the 16 school weeks during which the three teaching programmes were delivered. Following this test, all children were switched to the synthetic phonics programme. Finally, a second follow-up spelling test was applied at the end of the second school year.

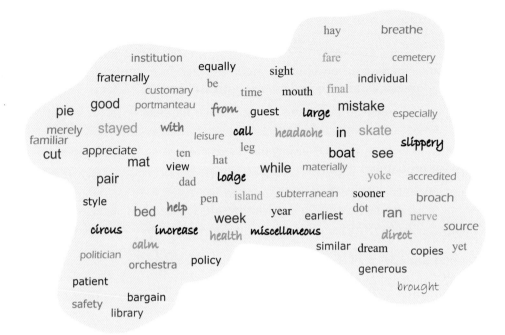

Some of the words used in the Schonell Spelling Test

---

**Example 8**    *Spelling at baseline*

The data obtained in the spelling tests at baseline are in Table 13. The categories across the columns are similar to those for the reading test: 'Higher' in this case means 'spelling age at baseline test higher than chronological age'.

**Table 13**    Results from the spelling test at baseline

|  | Spelling age as compared to chronological age | | |
|---|---|---|---|
|  | Not higher | Higher | Total |
| Analytic phonics | 57 | 51 | 108 |
| Analytic phonics + PA | 43 | 35 | 78 |
| Synthetic phonics | 70 | 47 | 117 |
| Total | 170 | 133 | 303 |

Consider the data from Table 13. Let $S_0$ denote the event 'spelling age higher than chronological age at the baseline test'.

Then

$$P(AP) = \frac{108}{303} \simeq 0.356.$$

Also,

$$P(S_0|AP) = \frac{51}{108} \simeq 0.472.$$

Hence

$$P(AP) \times P(S_0|AP) \simeq 0.356 \times 0.472$$
$$\simeq 0.168.$$

Note that this equals $P(S_0 \text{ and } AP)$ [and $P(AP \text{ and } S_0)$]:

$$P(S_0 \text{ and } AP) = \frac{51}{303} \simeq 0.168.$$

---

Activity 9 will give you some further practice at manipulating joint and conditional probabilities.

## Activity 9 *Calculating another joint probability*

In one school, 30% of sixth form students study physics. Of the students who study physics, 80% also study chemistry. If a student is picked at random, what is the probability that this student studies both physics and chemistry?

The relationship $P(A \text{ and } B) = P(B) \times P(A|B)$ can be rearranged so as to obtain

$$P(A|B) = \frac{P(A \text{ and } B)}{P(B)}.$$

This provides a convenient way of obtaining the conditional probability $P(A|B)$ when the joint probability $P(A \text{ and } B)$ and the probability $P(B)$ are known. Activity 10 will give you some more practice at manipulating joint and conditional probabilities in this way.

## Activity 10 *Comparing spelling at baseline*

Use the data in Table 13 as follows.

(a) Calculate $P(S_0|AP+)$ and $P(S_0|SP)$ directly from the table.

(b) Now derive these probabilities using the general relationship $P(A|B) = P(A \text{ and } B)/P(B)$, and check your results are the same as in part (a). (Make sure you keep full calculator accuracy for intermediate results.)

(c) Using these results and Example 8, comment briefly on any apparent differences in spelling ability at baseline.

*You have now covered the material related to Screencast 1 for Unit 8 (see the M140 website).*

## 3.2   Adding probabilities

In Unit 6 (Subsection 2.2), you learned how to add probabilities of
mutually exclusive events: if events $A$ and $B$ are mutually exclusive, then

$$P(A \text{ or } B) = P(A) + P(B).$$

The 'or' linkage leads to the *addition* of probabilities. In this subsection,
this expression will be extended to encompass events that are not mutually
exclusive. (We shall find that subtraction can also be involved.)

---

**Example 9**   *Spelling and reading at first follow-up*

In the classroom

At the first follow-up in the Clackmannanshire study, after the children
had received 16 school weeks of teaching according to the three
programmes, they were tested again using the Schonell Spelling Test.

Table 14 shows the spelling test and reading test results together, using a
new variable 'Standardised spelling and reading ages at first follow-up
test'. This variable has four categories – a similar variable was used in
Table 6 (Subsection 2.2). The categories are Low/Low (spelling age and
reading age both not higher than chronological age), Low/High (spelling
age not higher and reading age higher than chronological age), High/Low
(spelling age higher and reading age not higher than chronological age)
and High/High (both spelling age and reading age higher than
chronological age).

**Table 14**   Spelling and reading ability at first follow-up test

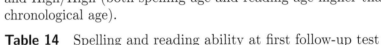

|  | Spelling/reading ages at first follow-up test | | | | |
|  | Low/Low | Low/High | High/Low | High/High | Total |
|---|---|---|---|---|---|
| Analytic phonics | 65 | 14 | 3 | 22 | 104 |
| Analytic phonics + PA | 42 | 8 | 9 | 16 | 75 |
| Synthetic phonics | 29 | 7 | 6 | 71 | 113 |
| Total | 136 | 29 | 18 | 109 | 292 |

Let $S_1$ denote the event 'spelling age higher than chronological age at first
follow-up test'. Consider the totals across the teaching groups at the
bottom of the table. A child did well in the spelling test if either the child
is in the High/Low category or in the High/High category. So as
$18 + 109 = 127$, that means 127 children out of the 292 did well in the
spelling test (that is, their spelling age was higher than their chronological
age), and so

$$P(S_1) = \frac{127}{292} \simeq 0.435.$$

A similar approach can be used for the different teaching groups. For
example, consider the probability that a child is either in the analytic
phonics ($AP$) group or in the analytic phonics + PA ($AP+$) group. As
$104 + 75 = 179$, there are 179 children out of 292 in either the $AP$ or $AP+$
group, so

$$P(AP \text{ or } AP+) = \frac{179}{292} \simeq 0.613.$$

Also,

$$P(AP) = \frac{104}{292} \simeq 0.356,$$

and

$$P(AP+) = \frac{75}{292} \simeq 0.257.$$

Thus $P(AP) + P(AP+) \simeq 0.613$. This equals $P(AP \text{ or } AP+)$, as expected, since the categories $AP$ and $AP+$ are mutually exclusive.

---

In Example 9, we considered probabilities of mutually exclusive events. But now consider the probability of being in the High/High ($HH$) category or in the synthetic phonics ($SP$) group, that is, the probability $P(HH \text{ or } SP)$.

From Table 14, there are 109 children in the High/High group, and 113 children in the $SP$ group. But the number in the '$HH$ or $SP$' group does not equal $109 + 113$, because there are 71 children who are in both the $HH$ group and the $SP$ group: these children would be double-counted. The number of children who are in either the $HH$ group or the $SP$ group (or both) is

$$22 + 16 + 71 + 6 + 7 + 29 = 109 + 113 - 71 = 151,$$

out of the total 292 children in the table.

Hence

$$\begin{aligned}
P(HH \text{ or } SP) &= P(HH) + P(SP) - P(HH \text{ and } SP) \\
&= \frac{109}{292} + \frac{113}{292} - \frac{71}{292} \\
&\simeq 0.517.
\end{aligned}$$

This is an instance of the general addition rule, highlighted below.

**The general addition rule for probabilities**

Let $A$ and $B$ denote two events, mutually exclusive or not. Then

$$P(A \text{ or } B) = P(A) + P(B) - P(A \text{ and } B).$$

Activity 11 gives you some practice at using the general rule for adding probabilities.

**Activity 11**   *Adding probabilities*

(a) In a school, 30% of sixth form students study physics, and 32% study chemistry. The proportion who study both physics and chemistry is 24%. What proportion of sixth form students in the school study physics or chemistry (or both)?

(b) A total of 291 children in the study took both the baseline and the first follow-up reading tests. Of these, 110 did well at the baseline test (that is, their reading age was higher than their chronological age), and 138 did well at the first follow-up test. Sixty children did well in both tests. Calculate the proportion of children who did well on either the baseline test or the first follow-up test.

(c) Among the children who did both the first and second follow-up reading tests, the proportions doing well (that is, with reading age higher than chronological age) were: 0.483 on the first test, 0.840 on the second test, and 0.848 on at least one of the tests. Calculate the proportion who did well on both tests. How many children among the 263 who did both tests did well on both?

## 3.3   Statistical independence and contingency tables

Recall from Unit 6 (Subsection 2.3) that two events are said to be *statistically independent* if the occurrence of one is unrelated to the chance of occurrence of the other.

In this subsection, we shall explore the notion of statistical independence as it applies to contingency tables. As before, we will use the Clackmannanshire study as an illustration.

**Example 10**   *Spelling at first and second follow-ups*

In Table 14 (Subsection 3.2) the joint results for spelling and reading at the first follow-up test were presented. We will now just concentrate on the spelling results. For ease of presentation, these are summarised in Table 15.

**Table 15**   Results from the spelling test at first follow-up

| | Spelling age as compared to chronological age | | |
| --- | --- | --- | --- |
| | Not higher | Higher | Total |
| Analytic phonics | 79 | 25 | 104 |
| Analytic phonics + PA | 50 | 25 | 75 |
| Synthetic phonics | 36 | 77 | 113 |
| Total | 165 | 127 | 292 |

The conditional probabilities of spelling age being higher than chronological age at the first follow-up are 0.240 (that is, 25/104) for the analytic phonics group, 0.333 (25/75) for the analytic phonics + PA group, and 0.681 (77/113) for the synthetic phonics group. These values are different. Recall that in Activity 10 (Subsection 3.1) you found these probabilities were broadly similar at baseline. So as with the reading test, there had been a great improvement in the synthetic phonics group, but not in the other two groups. Thus, on the face of it, it would appear that the teaching method may have influenced the outcome of the first spelling test. In other words, spelling ability and teaching method may not be independent. (We have to hedge such statements with 'appear that' and 'may not be', as we need to allow for the possibility that the observed pattern is entirely due to chance. After Section 4, you will be able to make much stronger statements!)

Note also that the conditional probabilities for each teaching group differ from the overall probability that a child who took the test at first follow-up did well at spelling, which is

$$P(S_1) = \frac{127}{292} \simeq 0.435.$$

After the first follow-up test, all children in the study were taught using the synthetic phonics method, and tested again at the end of the following school year. In Example 6 (at the beginning of this section), it was suggested that the children in the two analytic phonics groups had caught up with those in the synthetic phonics group, in terms of their reading ability. So, what about their spelling ability? This is shown in Table 16.

**Table 16**  Results from the spelling test at second follow-up

| | Spelling age as compared to chronological age | | |
| --- | --- | --- | --- |
| | Not higher | Higher | Total |
| Analytic phonics | 10 | 85 | 95 |
| Analytic phonics + PA | 7 | 59 | 66 |
| Synthetic phonics | 10 | 94 | 104 |
| Total | 27 | 238 | 265 |

In Activity 12 you will interpret these results. Let $S_2$ denote the event 'spelling age is higher than chronological age at the second-follow-up test'.

## Activity 12   *Interpreting the second follow-up spelling test results*

(a) Using Table 16, obtain the conditional probabilities $P(S_2|AP)$, $P(S_2|AP+)$ and $P(S_2|SP)$.

(b) Obtain the probability $P(S_2)$, using the marginal totals. (Recall that marginal totals were defined in Example 3, Subsection 2.1.)

(c) Compare these probabilities. In your view, has the teaching group (to which the children were originally allocated) influenced the outcome of the second spelling test? How might you explain this, in the light of the results of the spelling test at first follow-up?

In Example 10 and Activity 12, we compared conditional and marginal probabilities and arrived at judgements about possible dependence of test results on study group on that basis. This makes good sense more generally. If two events $A$ and $B$ are statistically independent, then conditioning on event $B$ will not affect the chance that $A$ occurs. This also works the other way around: conditioning on $A$ will not affect the chance that $B$ occurs.

So far, we have discussed statistical independence in terms of pairs of *events*. However, in Activity 12, the interpretation of the results was really in terms of the relationship between the variables 'teaching method' and 'spelling ability at the second test'; the events involved were just the values taken by those two variables. Thus, it makes sense to extend the notion of independence from pairs of events to pairs of *variables*: two variables are said to be statistically independent if there is no relationship between them, so that the value taken by either variable does not affect the value taken by the other variable. Thus, to say that the variables 'teaching method' and 'spelling ability at the second test' are independent means that the teaching method does not affect ability in the second follow-up spelling test, and vice versa.

### Independence and conditional probabilities

Two events $A$ and $B$ are statistically independent if the occurrence of one has no influence on the chance of occurrence of the other.

Moreover, they are independent exactly when

$$P(A|B) = P(A)$$

or (equivalently)

$$P(B|A) = P(B).$$

Two *variables* are said to be independent if the value taken by either variable does not influence the value taken by the other variable.

Activity 13 will give you some practice at recognising whether variables are independent.

## Activity 13    *Assessing independence*

In a school, 48% of sixth formers study both English and maths, 12% study maths but not English, 32% study English but not maths, and the remainder, 8%, study neither English nor maths. These percentages are shown as probabilities in Table 17.

**Table 17**    Proportions of students studying English and maths

|                      | Studying maths | Not studying maths |
|----------------------|:--------------:|:------------------:|
| Studying English     | 0.48           | 0.32               |
| Not studying English | 0.12           | 0.08               |

Let $E$ denote the event 'studies English', and $M$ the event 'studies maths'.

(a) Obtain the probabilities $P(E \text{ and } M)$, $P(E)$ and $P(M)$.

(b) Hence obtain the conditional probabilities $P(E|M)$ and $P(M|E)$.

(c) What do you conclude about the independence or otherwise of studying English and studying maths?

*You have now covered the material related to Screencast 2 for Unit 8 (see the M140 website).*

# Exercises on Section 3

**Exercise 4**    *Calculating probabilities from a contingency table*

Table 18 (which is the same as Table 9 in Exercises on Section 2) gives the numbers of boys and girls by teaching group in the Clackmannanshire study.

**Table 18**    Gender distribution by teaching group

|                        | Gender | | |
|------------------------|:----:|:----:|:-----:|
|                        | Boys | Girls | Total |
| Analytic phonics       | 58   | 51   | 109   |
| Analytic phonics + PA  | 39   | 39   | 78    |
| Synthetic phonics      | 61   | 56   | 117   |
| Total                  | 158  | 146  | 304   |

Let $B$ denote the event 'boy' and $G$ the event 'girl'. Calculate the following probabilities for the children in the study.

(a) $P(G|AP)$

(b) $P(AP+)$

(c) $P(SP|B)$

(d) $P(B \text{ and } AP+)$

(e)  The probability that a child allocated to the synthetic phonics group is a girl.

(f)  The probability that a boy is allocated to the analytic phonics group.

**Exercise 5**   *Calculating more probabilities*

Of the 264 children who did both the spelling and the reading test at the second follow-up, 237 had a spelling age higher than chronological age (event $S_2$), whereas 220 had a reading age higher than chronological age (event $R_2$). Furthermore, 214 children had both spelling age and reading age higher than chronological age.

(a)  Calculate $P(R_2|S_2)$.

(b)  Calculate the probability that a child who did well at reading also did well at spelling.

(c)  Calculate $P(R_2 \text{ or } S_2)$.

**Exercise 6**   *Are reading and spelling independent?*

Table 19 shows the $2 \times 2$ contingency table of spelling and reading ability at the second follow-up test. To simplify the row and column headings, we have used 'Low' to indicate that the measured age (for reading or spelling) is not higher than chronological age, and 'High' to indicate that it is higher.

**Table 19**   Spelling and reading ability at second follow-up test

|          |        | Reading age | | |
|----------|--------|-----|------|-------|
|          |        | Low | High | Total |
| Spelling | Low    | 21  | 6    | 27    |
| age      | High   | 23  | 214  | 237   |
|          | Total  | 44  | 220  | 264   |

(a)  Explain why Table 19 is a contingency table.

(b)  Obtain the probabilities $P(\text{Reading High}|\text{Spelling Low})$ and $P(\text{Reading High})$.

(c)  Compare these probabilities informally. Are the reading and spelling variables likely to be independent? What further information might you require?

# 4 The $\chi^2$ test for contingency tables

At several points in Sections 2 and 3, you have been invited to comment about an association, or lack of association, between teaching method and reading (or spelling) ability. Thus, for example, you found in Activity 3 (Subsection 2.1) that the proportions of children doing well at reading in the baseline test were similar in the three reading groups; in Activity 4 (Subsection 2.1), in contrast, you found differences between groups in reading ability at the first follow-up test. But at what point does 'similar' become 'different'? Any conclusions you might have been tempted to draw had to be qualified, owing to the possibility of chance fluctuations.

In this section, these issues are considered in detail. You will learn how to carry out the $\chi^2$ **test for contingency tables**. ($\chi^2$ is sometimes written as 'chi-squared' or 'chi-square' – particularly in situations where it is difficult to write the symbol '$\chi^2$'.) This test, first developed by Karl Pearson in 1900, provides a way of quantifying the likely effect of chance. We start by considering the hypotheses for the test.

Karl Pearson (1857–1936) is credited with founding the discipline of mathematical statistics. He also coined the term 'contingency table'.

Karl Pearson (1857–1936)

## 4.1 The null and alternative hypotheses

We shall consider how to formulate appropriate null and alternative hypotheses using some of the data encountered earlier. But first, it's important to be clear that hypothesis tests cannot directly tell you *why* variables might be related, but only *whether* they are related. So, for example, hypothesis testing cannot tell you that the presence of one factor causes another to occur.

---

**Example 11**   *Taking care with hypotheses*

Table 3 (Subsection 2.1) showed how the sample of children in the Clackmannanshire study performed at the first follow-up reading test. The question of interest is whether teaching method, represented by the categories determining the rows of the table, has any impact on reading ability, represented by the categories in the columns. So, it would seem that one way of expressing the null and alternative hypotheses could be:

$H_0$: Teaching method has no effect on the reading ability at the first follow-up test of children starting at primary school.

$H_1$: Teaching method does affect the reading ability at the first follow-up test of children starting at primary school.

As usual, the hypotheses relate to the whole population of children learning how to read, not to the ones that happened to be selected for the sample. 'Teaching method', on the other hand, refers to the three methods investigated in the study.

This form of the alternative hypothesis implies that teaching method *causes* the child to score differently in the reading test. However, the hypothesis test that we develop does *not* actually investigate this. Rather, it examines whether teaching method and reading ability are associated. A more accurate way of expressing the hypotheses, which implies nothing about causality, will be discussed below.

The contrast between causality and association is discussed in Subsection 5.1.

In Activity 4 (Subsection 2.1), you calculated the percentages of children in each teaching group with a reading age higher than chronological age. The corresponding proportions are shown in Table 20.

**Table 20**   Results from the first follow-up test

|  | Reading age as compared to chronological age | |
|  | Proportion not higher | Proportion higher |
| --- | --- | --- |
| Analytic phonics | 0.654 | 0.346 |
| Analytic phonics + PA | 0.680 | 0.320 |
| Synthetic phonics | 0.310 | 0.690 |

The proportions add up to 1 across rows, and vary as we read down each column of Table 20.

What we want to know is whether these differences are due to sampling or whether there are 'real' differences which are associated with the teaching method. If the study had been repeated in a different year, with different children, or choosing different schools, we would not expect the results to be exactly the same as in Table 20. However, we should expect them to be fairly similar, as the values were obtained from quite large samples and from a number of schools. What we want to do is to make an inference from the sample back to the population.

Thus, we are interested in the reading ability of the population of all children starting at primary school, and whether they would have the same distribution of reading abilities, whatever teaching method they had been taught by. In other words, we want to know whether teaching method and reading ability are independent.

This leads to the following form for the null and alternative hypotheses.

$H_0$: Teaching method for children starting at primary school and reading ability at the first follow-up test are independent.

$H_1$: Teaching method for children starting at primary school and reading ability at the first follow-up test are not independent.

This formulation of the hypotheses avoids any suggestion of causality. Activity 14 will give you some practice at formulating null and alternative hypotheses.

**Activity 14**   *Formulating hypotheses*

As discussed in Example 2 (Subsection 2.1), the baseline reading test was designed to find out whether there are any differences in reading ability between teaching groups before the different teaching methods were applied, because differences other than those due to chance could bias subsequent comparisons. Table 21 shows the observed proportions.

**Table 21**   Results from the baseline test

| | Reading age as compared to chronological age | |
| | Proportion not higher | Proportion higher |
| --- | --- | --- |
| Analytic phonics | 0.639 | 0.361 |
| Analytic phonics + PA | 0.551 | 0.449 |
| Synthetic phonics | 0.650 | 0.350 |

Write down the null and alternative hypotheses to test whether there is any relationship between teaching method and reading ability at baseline.

## 4.2   Calculating the Expected values

In Unit 5 (Subsection 3.2) the DFR equation was introduced, which connects 'Data', 'Fit' and 'Residual'. In this section, we shall use slightly different terminology, which is standard for contingency tables. Thus, 'Data' will be called 'Observed', and 'Fit' will be called 'Expected'. This is because the 'Fit' values are those that one would expect if the null hypothesis of independence were true. The test to be described in this subsection is based on the following form of the DFR equation,

Residual = Observed − Expected.

The idea behind the test is as follows. If the null hypothesis is true, then the 'Expected' values should be close to the 'Observed' values, because these 'Expected' values are obtained assuming the null hypothesis is true. Thus, the residuals should be small if the null hypothesis is true. Consequently, if some of these residuals are large, it suggests that the null hypothesis is false. The $\chi^2$ test statistic will be based on the sizes of the residuals.

The first step in calculating the $\chi^2$ test statistic is to obtain the 'Expected' values. One way to do this is described in Example 12.

**Example 12**   *Expected values for reading at first follow-up*

We will use the contingency table of reading ability at the first follow-up test, given initially in Table 3 (Subsection 2.1) and reproduced below as Table 22.

**Table 22**   Results from the first follow-up test

|  | Reading age as compared to chronological age | | |
|---|---|---|---|
|  | Not higher | Higher | Total |
| Analytic phonics | 68 | 36 | 104 |
| Analytic phonics + PA | 51 | 24 | 75 |
| Synthetic phonics | 35 | 78 | 113 |
| Total | 154 | 138 | 292 |

We shall calculate the Expected values based on the null hypothesis of independence. This is as follows (for completeness we also state the alternative hypothesis):

$H_0$: Teaching method for children starting at primary school and reading ability at the first follow-up test are independent.

$H_1$: Teaching method for children starting at primary school and reading ability at the first follow-up test are not independent.

Under the null hypothesis of independence, the population distributions of reading ability are the same in each teaching group. So we can combine reading groups and use the column totals in Table 22 to calculate the proportions of children whose reading age is higher, or not higher, than chronological age.

Thus, under the null hypothesis,

$$P(\text{Reading age not higher than chronological age}) = \frac{154}{292},$$

and

$$P(\text{Reading age higher than chronological age}) = \frac{138}{292}.$$

We have not expressed these numbers as decimals as we are about to use them in calculations, and it's best to keep them as fractions. (You can of course use decimals, in which case make sure that you keep full calculator accuracy.)

Since there are 104 children in the analytic phonics group, then under the null hypothesis we would expect a proportion 154/292 of them to have reading age not higher than chronological age, and a proportion 138/292 to have reading age higher than chronological age.

Thus, the Expected values for the analytic phonics group are:

$$\text{Not higher: } 104 \times \frac{154}{292} \simeq 54.8493, \quad \text{Higher: } 104 \times \frac{138}{292} \simeq 49.1507.$$

Note that Expected values are not, in general, whole numbers. This is because they are not counts, but expected frequencies.

In Activity 15, you are invited to complete the Expected table using the method described in Example 12.

**Activity 15** *Completing the Expected table*

Use the marginal counts in Table 22 to obtain the Expected values (to four decimal places):

(a) for the analytic phonics + PA group

(b) for the synthetic phonics group.

The Expected values obtained in Example 12 and Activity 15 are displayed in Table 23. (For brevity, the top heading of the results table is not included here. We will continue to use this abbreviated style for Expected and Residual tables.)

**Table 23** Expected table for reading ability at first follow-up

|  | Not higher | Higher | Total |
| --- | --- | --- | --- |
| Analytic phonics | 54.8493 | 49.1507 | 104.0000 |
| Analytic phonics + PA | 39.5548 | 35.4452 | 75.0000 |
| Synthetic phonics | 59.5959 | 53.4041 | 113.0000 |
| Total | 154.0000 | 138.0000 | 292.0000 |

Note that the marginal totals for the Expected table are the same as for the Observed table. This is no coincidence, but follows from the way the Expected values were calculated. (Occasionally some small discrepancies might occur, owing to rounding.)

The calculation of Expected values is summarised in the following box.

**Calculating the Expected values**

For each cell in a contingency table, the Expected values under the null hypothesis of independence are obtained as follows from the marginal totals:

$$\text{Expected value} = \frac{\text{row total} \times \text{column total}}{\text{overall total}}.$$

Activity 16 will give you some practice at calculating Expected values. A convenient way to do the calculations is to copy the marginal totals of the Observed table into the Expected table. Then calculate the Expected values from these marginal totals, and finally check that the Expected values add up to the marginal totals (apart from rounding error).

**Activity 16**  *Calculating Expected values for reading at baseline*

Obtain the Expected values (to four decimal places) for the contingency table of baseline reading test results in Table 2 (Subsection 2.1), reproduced here as Table 24. (This is the table of Observed values.)

**Table 24**  Observed results from the baseline test

|  | Reading age as compared to chronological age | | |
|---|---|---|---|
|  | Not higher | Higher | Total |
| Analytic phonics | 69 | 39 | 108 |
| Analytic phonics + PA | 43 | 35 | 78 |
| Synthetic phonics | 76 | 41 | 117 |
| Total | 188 | 115 | 303 |

*You have now covered the material related to Screencast 3 for Unit 8 (see the M140 website).*

Having waited in all day, Percy's mood
was worsened even further when the furniture
company finally turned up–and delivered a new
sofa instead of the expected table.

## 4.3 Calculating the $\chi^2$ test statistic

As stated at the beginning of Subsection 4.2, the $\chi^2$ test statistic is based on the residuals. Having obtained the Expected values under the null hypothesis of independence, the next stage is to obtain the Residual table. This is described in Example 13.

---

**Example 13**  *Residuals for reading at first follow-up*

In Subsection 4.2, the Observed values are in Table 22, and the Expected values are in Table 23. The Residual table is obtained using the DFR equation in the form

Residual = Observed − Expected.

For example, the entry in the Residual table for the cell corresponding to 'Not higher' in the analytic phonics group is

$68 - 54.8493 = 13.1507.$

The other entries are calculated in a similar fashion, resulting in Table 25.

**Table 25**  Residual table for reading ability at first follow-up

|  | Not higher | Higher | Total |
|---|---|---|---|
| Analytic phonics | 13.1507 | −13.1507 | 0.0000 |
| Analytic phonics + PA | 11.4452 | −11.4452 | 0.0000 |
| Synthetic phonics | −24.5959 | 24.5959 | 0.0000 |
| Total | 0.0000 | 0.0000 | 0.0000 |

Note that the rows and the columns add to zero (subject to rounding). This follows from the fact that the Observed and Expected tables have the same marginal totals.

---

The test statistic is based not on the residuals directly, but on a measure of their magnitude relative to the Expected values, called the $\chi^2$ **contributions**. For each cell we calculate the quantity

$$\chi^2 \text{ contribution} = \frac{(\text{Observed} - \text{Expected})^2}{\text{Expected}}.$$

There are sound mathematical reasons for using this particular formula. For example, the reason we square the residuals in this way is that we are interested in their departure from zero, in either the positive or negative direction, both providing evidence against the null hypothesis. And the reason we divide by the Expected value is to allow for differences in the magnitudes of these Expected values. Note that the $\chi^2$ contributions must always be positive, or zero: they cannot be negative.

Finally, the $\chi^2$ test statistic is obtained by summing the $\chi^2$ contributions. These steps of the calculation are illustrated in Example 14.

**Example 14**   *Calculating $\chi^2$ test statistic for reading at first follow-up*

The Expected and Residual values in Table 23 (Subsection 4.2) and Table 25, respectively, are combined to obtain the contributions to $\chi^2$. Thus, for the cell corresponding to 'Not higher' in the analytic phonics group,

$$\chi^2 \text{ contribution} = \frac{(\text{Observed} - \text{Expected})^2}{\text{Expected}}$$

$$= \frac{\text{Residual}^2}{\text{Expected}}$$

$$= \frac{13.1507^2}{54.8493}$$

$$\simeq 3.1530.$$

Repeating the calculation for all six cells results in the $\chi^2$ contributions table (or $\chi^2$ table, for short) in Table 26.

**Table 26**   $\chi^2$ contributions table for reading ability at first follow-up

|  | Not higher | Higher |
|---|---|---|
| Analytic phonics | 3.1530 | 3.5186 |
| Analytic phonics + PA | 3.3117 | 3.6956 |
| Synthetic phonics | 10.1510 | 11.3279 |

Finally, the $\chi^2$ test statistic is obtained by summing the six $\chi^2$ contributions:

$$\chi^2 = 3.1530 + 3.5186 + 3.3117 + 3.6956 + 10.1510 + 11.3279$$

$$= 35.1578.$$

The final value of the test statistic, rounded to three decimal places, is 35.158.

These steps of the calculation are summarised in the following box.

**Calculating the $\chi^2$ test statistic**

From the Observed ($O$) and Expected ($E$) tables, obtain the residuals $O - E$, and hence the $\chi^2$ contributions:

$$\chi^2 \text{ contribution} = \frac{(O - E)^2}{E}.$$

The $\chi^2$ test statistic is the sum of the $\chi^2$ contributions over all the cells in the contingency table:

$$\chi^2 = \sum \frac{(O - E)^2}{E}.$$

Activity 17 will give you some practice at these calculations.

**Activity 17**    *Calculating $\chi^2$ test statistic for reading at baseline*

In Activity 16 (Subsection 4.2) you calculated the Expected values for the contingency table of reading ability at the baseline test. These values, along with the Observed marginal totals, are reproduced in Table 27.

**Table 27**    Expected values for the baseline test data

|  | Not higher | Higher | Total |
| --- | --- | --- | --- |
| Analytic phonics | 67.0099 | 40.9901 | 108 |
| Analytic phonics + PA | 48.3960 | 29.6040 | 78 |
| Synthetic phonics | 72.5941 | 44.4059 | 117 |
| Total | 188 | 115 | 303 |

Use these values to obtain the following.

(a) Obtain the $\chi^2$ contributions, using the Observed values in Table 24.

(b) Hence obtain the $\chi^2$ test statistic.

*You have now covered the material related to Screencast 4 for Unit 8 (see the M140 website).*

## 4.4   Interpreting the $\chi^2$ test statistic

The $\chi^2$ test statistic was constructed in such a way that large positive values provide evidence against the null hypothesis of independence between the row and column variables whose categories define the contingency table. But how can we make this more precise?

In fact, if the null hypothesis is true, then the approximate probability distribution of the $\chi^2$ statistic is known: it is a member of the $\chi^2$ **family of distributions**. Choosing the right reference distribution among this family will be considered after the next example.

**Example 15**   *Interpreting $\chi^2$ test statistic for reading at first follow-up*

From Example 14 (Subsection 4.3), the $\chi^2$ test statistic for the $3 \times 2$ contingency table of teaching method by reading ability at the first follow-up test is 35.158. If the null hypothesis were true, this test statistic would have the particular $\chi^2$ distribution shown in Figure 3.

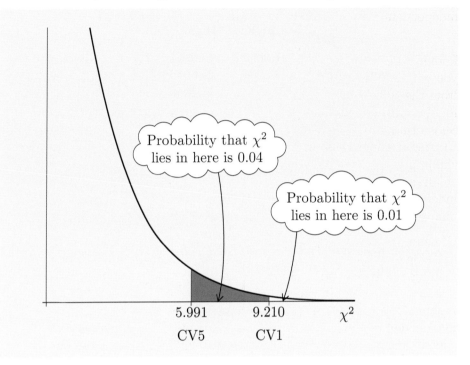

**Figure 3**   Probability distribution of the test statistic for reading ability at the first follow-up test, with critical values

Also shown in Figure 3 is the critical value CV5 corresponding to the 5% significance level, and the critical value CV1 corresponding to the 1% significance level. (Critical values were discussed in Units 6 and 7.) The 5% and 1% critical values are

$$\text{CV5} = 5.991, \qquad \text{CV1} = 9.210.$$

The test procedure we use is very similar to that for the $z$-test described in Unit 7:

- Reject $H_0$ at the 1% significance level if $\chi^2 \geq 9.210$.
- Reject $H_0$ at the 5% significance level if $\chi^2 \geq 5.991$.
- Do not reject $H_0$ if $\chi^2 < 5.991$.

(If $5.991 \leq \chi^2 < 9.210$, then we reject $H_0$ at the 5% but not at the 1% significance level.)

Applying this rule, since in our case $\chi^2 = 35.158 \geq 9.210$, we reject the null hypothesis at the 1% significance level. To interpret this decision, we refer back to our hypotheses in Subsection 4.1. These were:

$H_0$: Teaching method for children starting at primary school and reading ability at the first follow-up test are independent.

$H_1$: Teaching method for children starting at primary school and reading ability at the first follow-up test are not independent.

We therefore conclude that the method used to teach children starting at primary school and their reading ability at the first follow-up test are not independent – that is, they are related.

---

Looking again at the table of $\chi^2$ contributions (Table 26, Subsection 4.3), you will see that the biggest contributions to the $\chi^2$ test statistic come from the synthetic phonics group. Now look at the signs of the residuals for the synthetic phonics group in the Residual table (Table 25, Subsection 4.3). The signs are negative for 'Not higher' and positive for 'Higher', indicating that, in the synthetic phonics group, there are fewer children whose reading age is not higher than chronological age, and more children whose reading age is higher, than would be the case under independence. Thus, the departure from independence appears to be mainly due to the higher ability of the synthetic phonics group.

Of course, you can also see this directly in this case: the data (first given in Table 3, Subsection 2.1) show that the proportion of children with reading age greater than chronological age is much higher in the synthetic phonics group than in the two other groups. However, with larger tables, it is sometimes more difficult to pin down where a departure from independence comes from, and in that case looking at the large $\chi^2$ contributions and the signs of the corresponding residuals can help.

Example 15 shows that random fluctuations are unlikely to account for the better reading ability of the children in the synthetic phonics group at the first follow-up test. What about the baseline test? This is the topic of Activity 18.

## Activity 18   Interpreting $\chi^2$ statistic for reading at baseline

In Activity 17 (Subsection 4.3), you found that the $\chi^2$ test statistic for the test of independence was 2.162. The critical values for the test are CV5 = 9.210 and CV1 = 5.991, as in Example 15.

Use this information to test the null hypothesis of independence between teaching group and reading ability in the baseline test. State your conclusions.

---

One final piece of the jigsaw remains to be put in place: choosing which member of the family of $\chi^2$ distributions to use as reference for the test, and finding its critical values. The particular $\chi^2$ distribution to use, and hence the critical values, depend on the **degrees of freedom** of the contingency table. These, in turn, depend on the size of the table.

For an $r \times c$ table, with $r$ rows and $c$ columns,

degrees of freedom $= (r - 1) \times (c - 1)$.

For example, for a $3 \times 2$ table, $r = 3$ and $c = 2$, so

degrees of freedom $= (3 - 1) \times (2 - 1) = 2$.

Figure 4 shows the $\chi^2$ probability distributions for several different values of the degrees of freedom.

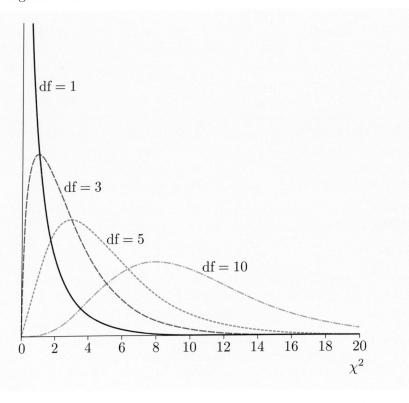

**Figure 4**   $\chi^2$ probability distributions for degrees of freedom (df) 1, 3, 5, 10

Once you have worked out the degrees of freedom, you can look up the critical values CV5 and CV1 in statistical tables. A subset of the relevant table of critical values is given in Table 28.

**Table 28**   Table of critical values of $\chi^2$

| Degrees of freedom | Critical values of $\chi^2$ at significance level | |
|---|---|---|
| | 5% | 1% |
| 1 | 3.841 | 6.635 |
| 2 | 5.991 | 9.210 |
| 3 | 7.815 | 11.345 |
| 4 | 9.488 | 13.277 |
| 5 | 11.070 | 15.086 |
| 6 | 12.592 | 16.812 |
| 7 | 14.067 | 18.475 |
| 8 | 15.507 | 20.090 |
| 9 | 16.919 | 21.666 |
| 10 | 18.307 | 23.209 |
| 11 | 19.675 | 24.725 |
| 12 | 21.026 | 26.217 |

Activity 19 will give you some practice at finding critical values.

## Activity 19    *Finding critical values*

Find the degrees of freedom and the critical values at significance levels 1% and 5% for contingency tables with the following sizes.

(a)  $2 \times 2$

(b)  $4 \times 3$

(c)  $5 \times 4$

(d)  $4 \times 2$

### Tilting at windmills

When Karl Pearson first proposed the $\chi^2$ test in 1900, he incorrectly specified that the degrees of freedom for an $r \times c$ contingency table should be $(r \times c) - 1$, rather than $(r - 1) \times (c - 1)$. For example, he would have given 8 rather than 4 as the degrees of freedom of a $3 \times 3$ contingency table. That all was not well was first noticed by statisticians Major Greenwood and Udny Yule in 1915, though they did not come up with a solution. This was provided in 1922 by the eminent statistician R. A. Fisher. Pearson did not accept he was wrong, and published a robust rebuttal in which he likened Fisher, whom he could not bring himself to name, to Don Quixote tilting at windmills. But Fisher was right: the correct number of degrees of freedom is $(r - 1) \times (c - 1)$.

Ronald Aylmer Fisher
(1890–1962)

*You have now covered the material related to Screencast 5 for Unit 8 (see the M140 website).*

## 4.5  Putting it all together

In this subsection we bring together the various steps involved in carrying out the $\chi^2$ test. These are set out in the following box, and also in the flow diagram in Figure 5.

---

**Procedure: the $\chi^2$ test for contingency tables**

1.  Set up the null and alternative hypotheses in terms of the independence or otherwise of the row and column variables.

2.  From the Observed table, calculate the Expected, Residual and $\chi^2$ contribution tables.

3.  Calculate the $\chi^2$ test statistic by summing all the $\chi^2$ contributions.

4.  Find the degrees of freedom: $(r-1) \times (c-1)$. Look up the critical values at the 5% and 1% significance levels (CV5 and CV1).

5.  Compare $\chi^2$ with CV5 and CV1.

    •  If $\chi^2 \geq \text{CV1}$, then $H_0$ is rejected at the 1% significance level.

    •  If $\text{CV5} \leq \chi^2 < \text{CV1}$, then $H_0$ is rejected at the 5% significance level but not at the 1% significance level.

    •  If $\chi^2 < \text{CV5}$, then $H_0$ is not rejected at the 5% significance level.

6.  State your conclusion in non-mathematical terms.

---

As we saw after Example 15 (Subsection 4.4), if the null hypothesis is rejected, it can be helpful to look at the tables of $\chi^2$ contributions and residuals to see in what way the two variables are not independent. First, look at the $\chi^2$ contributions and pick out the large terms. These indicate which cells show a marked departure from independence. Then look at the residuals for these cells: their sign indicates the direction of the dependence.

In the remainder of this subsection, you will apply the $\chi^2$ test to other results from the Clackmannanshire study. So far, you have seen that the baseline reading test results did not indicate any dependence between the reading group and reading ability prior to teaching commencing. However, reading ability at the first follow-up test did show such a dependence (at the 1% significance level), and indicated that children in the synthetic phonics group were performing better.

In Activity 20 you will investigate whether this relationship persisted at the second follow-up test, after all children had been taught by the synthetic phonics method.

In this and subsequent activities and exercises, you should keep four decimal places in intermediate calculations, and round the $\chi^2$ statistic to three decimal places.

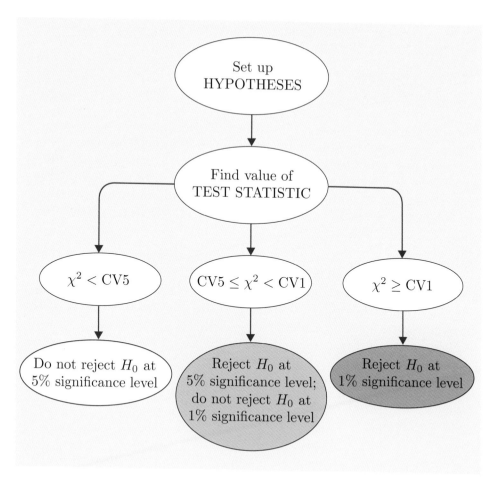

**Figure 5** Flow diagram for the $\chi^2$ test

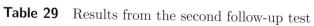

**Activity 20** *Testing for independence: reading at second follow-up*

The results of the second follow-up test were presented in Table 12 (Section 3), reproduced here as Table 29.

**Table 29** Results from the second follow-up test

| | Reading age as compared to chronological age | | |
| --- | --- | --- | --- |
| | Not higher | Higher | Total |
| Analytic phonics | 19 | 78 | 97 |
| Analytic phonics + PA | 11 | 55 | 66 |
| Synthetic phonics | 15 | 90 | 105 |
| Total | 45 | 223 | 268 |

(a) Write down the null and alternative hypotheses (the two variables are: teaching method originally allocated, and reading ability).

(b) Obtain the Expected table.

(c) Hence obtain the Residual and $\chi^2$ contributions tables.

(d) Calculate the $\chi^2$ test statistic and note the appropriate critical values, CV5 and CV1 (use Table 28 in Subsection 4.4).

(e) State your conclusions.

Thus, by the second follow-up test, the difference between the teaching groups has disappeared. Looking at Table 29, it is clear that by the second follow-up test, the three groups of children are performing equally well, and a large proportion of children in each group now have a reading age higher than their chronological age. One interpretation is that switching the children in the two analytic phonics groups to synthetic phonics has allowed them to catch up.

A restriction of the $\chi^2$ test, which we have not mentioned so far, is that it should not be used when some of the Expected values are small. This is because the calculation of the critical values is based on approximations which hold only when the Expected values are reasonably large. In M140, we shall use the following rule:

**The Expected $\geq$ 5 rule**

The $\chi^2$ test should be used *only* when all Expected values are *greater than or equal to 5*.

The number 5 in this rule is a little arbitrary. There are other rules that are less restrictive, but this is the most commonly used one, so it makes sense to use it for M140. The rule applies only to the Expected values: the $\chi^2$ test still applies if the Observed values are small.

Example 16 gives an example where the rule is violated, and describes a way round the problem by combining categories.

**Example 16**    *Revisiting spelling and reading at first follow-up*

In Example 9 (Subsection 3.2) data were presented on ability in both spelling and reading at the first test. The data from Table 14, introduced in that example, are reproduced here as Table 30.

**Table 30**    Spelling and reading ability at first follow-up test

| | Spelling/reading ages at first follow-up test | | | | |
| | Low/Low | Low/High | High/Low | High/High | Total |
|---|---|---|---|---|---|
| Analytic phonics | 65 | 14 | 3 | 22 | 104 |
| Analytic phonics + PA | 42 | 8 | 9 | 16 | 75 |
| Synthetic phonics | 29 | 7 | 6 | 71 | 113 |
| Total | 136 | 29 | 18 | 109 | 292 |

The corresponding table of Expected values is shown in Table 31.

**Table 31**  Expected values for spelling and reading ability at first follow-up

|  | Low/Low | Low/High | High/Low | High/High |
|---|---|---|---|---|
| Analytic phonics | 48.4384 | 10.3288 | 6.4110 | 38.8219 |
| Analytic phonics + PA | 34.9315 | 7.4486 | 4.6233 | 27.9966 |
| Synthetic phonics | 52.6301 | 11.2226 | 6.9658 | 42.1815 |

The Expected value corresponding to the High/Low category within the analytic phonics + PA group is 4.6233, and thus violates the rule. Hence, the results of the $\chi^2$ test applied to this table may be unreliable.

One way to get round this problem is to combine categories. There is no general way to do this: some combinations are sensible, others less so. In the present case, we could combine the analytic phonics and analytic phonics + PA groups into a single 'any analytic phonics' group, so as to retain the contrast between methods based on analytic and synthetic phonics. (An alternative combination is explored in Exercise 9.)

Combining categories should only be done if it makes sense. If the contingency table is of size $2 \times 2$, then combining categories is not possible. For example, if the two rows were combined you would no longer have a contingency table. (There is a test which you can apply in these circumstances, but it is not covered in M140.)

In Activity 21 you are asked to apply the $\chi^2$ test to Table 30 with the two analytic phonics groups combined. This will produce a $2 \times 4$ table. The $\chi^2$ test applies to tables of any dimensions $r \geq 2$, $c \geq 2$.

**Activity 21**   *Testing for independence: using combined groups*

In Example 16 it was suggested that the two groups 'analytic phonics' and 'analytic phonics + PA' should be combined into a new teaching group, 'any analytic phonics'. These data are shown in Table 32.

**Table 32**  Spelling and reading ability at first follow-up test

|  | Spelling/reading ages at first follow-up test | | | | |
|---|---|---|---|---|---|
|  | Low/Low | Low/High | High/Low | High/High | Total |
| Any analytic phonics | 107 | 22 | 12 | 38 | 179 |
| Synthetic phonics | 29 | 7 | 6 | 71 | 113 |
| Total | 136 | 29 | 18 | 109 | 292 |

(a)  Write down the null and alternative hypotheses (the two variables are: teaching method, and ability in spelling/reading).

(b)  Obtain the Expected table. Check that all Expected values are $\geq 5$.

(c)  Obtain the Residual and $\chi^2$ contributions tables.

(d) Calculate the $\chi^2$ test statistic and note the appropriate critical values, CV5 and CV1 (use Table 28 in Subsection 4.4).

(e) State your conclusions.

(f) If you reject the null hypothesis, describe the relationship you observe.

In this section we have developed the $\chi^2$ hypothesis test for contingency tables, and applied it to data from the Clackmannanshire study. In the next section we shall look a little more closely at causality, and also consider some reservations about both the data and the hypothesis test.

*You have now covered the material related to Screencast 6 for Unit 8 (see the M140 website).*

## Exercises on Section 4

**Exercise 7**   *Testing for independence: spelling at first follow-up*

The results on spelling ability at the first follow-up test were presented in Table 15 (Subsection 3.3), reproduced here as Table 33.

**Table 33**   Results from the spelling test at first follow-up

|  | Spelling age as compared to chronological age | | |
|  | Not higher | Higher | Total |
| --- | --- | --- | --- |
| Analytic phonics | 79 | 25 | 104 |
| Analytic phonics + PA | 50 | 25 | 75 |
| Synthetic phonics | 36 | 77 | 113 |
| Total | 165 | 127 | 292 |

(a) Write down the null and alternative hypotheses.

(b) Obtain the Expected table.

(c) Hence obtain the Residual and $\chi^2$ contribution tables.

(d) Calculate the $\chi^2$ test statistic and note the appropriate critical values, CV5 and CV1.

(e) State your conclusions.

(f) If you reject the null hypothesis, describe the relationship you observe.

**Exercise 8**   *Testing for independence: spelling at second follow-up*

The results on spelling ability at the second follow-up test were presented in Table 16 (Subsection 3.3), reproduced here as Table 34.

**Table 34**   Results from the spelling test at second follow-up

| | Spelling age as compared to chronological age | | |
| | Not higher | Higher | Total |
| --- | --- | --- | --- |
| Analytic phonics | 10 | 85 | 95 |
| Analytic phonics + PA | 7 | 59 | 66 |
| Synthetic phonics | 10 | 94 | 104 |
| Total | 27 | 238 | 265 |

(a) Write down the null and alternative hypotheses. (The variables are: teaching method originally allocated, and spelling ability at the second follow-up test.)

(b) Obtain the Expected table.

(c) Hence obtain the Residual and $\chi^2$ contributions tables.

(d) Calculate the $\chi^2$ test statistic and note the appropriate critical values, CV5 and CV1.

(e) State your conclusions.

**Exercise 9**   *Spelling and reading: combining categories*

In Example 16 (Subsection 4.5), it was suggested that the two analytic phonics groups in Table 30 should be combined in order to make all Expected values greater than 5; you performed the corresponding $\chi^2$ test in Activity 21. An alternative is to combine the Low/High and High/Low categories, thus resulting in the data shown in Table 35.

**Table 35**   Spelling and reading ability at first follow-up test

| | Spelling/reading ages at first follow-up test | | | |
| | Low/Low | Low/High or High/Low | High/High | Total |
| --- | --- | --- | --- | --- |
| Analytic phonics | 65 | 17 | 22 | 104 |
| Analytic phonics + PA | 42 | 17 | 16 | 75 |
| Synthetic phonics | 29 | 13 | 71 | 113 |
| Total | 136 | 47 | 109 | 292 |

(a) Write down the null and alternative hypotheses. (The variables are: teaching method, and spelling/reading ability at the first follow-up test.)

(b) Obtain the Expected table. Check that the Expected values are all greater than or equal to 5.

(c) Hence obtain the Residual and $\chi^2$ contributions tables.

(d) Calculate the $\chi^2$ test statistic and note the appropriate critical values, CV5 and CV1.

(e) State your conclusions.

(f) If you reject the null hypothesis, describe the relationship you observe.

# 5 More about the $\chi^2$ test

In this section, some further aspects of the $\chi^2$ test are considered. In fact, much of the material in this section applies more generally to hypothesis tests other than the $\chi^2$ test. However, we shall use the $\chi^2$ test as the focus of the discussion and, specifically, its application to the theme of this unit, namely the evaluation of different methods for teaching how to read.

The story so far may be summarised as follows. The Clackmannanshire study was undertaken to compare three methods for teaching how to read: analytic phonics, analytic phonics plus phonological awareness (PA), and synthetic phonics. To this end, 13 classes of children entering primary schools in Clackmannanshire were assigned to one of the three study methods. Before the teaching began, the children were tested on a range of abilities, including reading and spelling. At this stage, there were no significant differences between the three groups (as demonstrated by a $\chi^2$ test at the 5% significance level). The children were retested after 16 teaching weeks. At this stage, there were significant differences in reading and spelling ability between the three groups (as shown by a $\chi^2$ test at the 1% level), the children allocated to the synthetic phonics programme having performed much better than those on the two analytic phonics programmes. In consequence, all children were thereafter taught using synthetic phonics. A second follow-up test was done at the end of the second school year. A further $\chi^2$ test on these data (at the 5% level) revealed no differences between the three groups: all three performed equally well. Our interpretation (see comment after Activity 20 in Subsection 4.5) was that the children originally allocated to the two analytic phonics groups had 'caught up'.

This, however, is but *one* interpretation of the findings. The $\chi^2$ test does not tell us how to interpret these findings. It can only tell us that, at the second follow-up, there is no significant difference between the three groups. It does not tell us *why* there is no difference, just as it did not tell us *why* a difference had appeared at the first follow-up test.

## 5.1  Causality and association

Of course, what we really want to know is whether synthetic phonics is a better method of teaching, that is, whether it *helps* children to learn how to read better than the other two methods. But no hypothesis test can, on its own, demonstrate causality or the lack of it. It can only provide evidence of a relationship or association between variables, and cannot show that a change in one variable *causes* a change in the other.

For example, another interpretation of the results at the second follow-up test could be that the children in the analytic phonics group would have 'caught up' anyway, whatever the teaching method. Under this interpretation, the early advantage of the synthetic phonics group at the first follow-up test does not persist: in the long term there is no difference between the methods.

In order to investigate these and other issues, a further comparative study was undertaken to compare the children (now aged 10) taught primarily by synthetic phonics in the original Clackmannanshire study, with an otherwise similar group of children of the same age who had been taught primarily using analytic phonics. The data in this subsection come from this further study, which we shall call the Long Term study. (Johnston, R., McGeown, S. and Watson, J. (2012) 'Long-term effects of synthetic versus analytic phonics teaching on the reading and spelling ability of 10 year old boys and girls', *Reading and Writing: An Interdisciplinary Journal*, vol. 25, pp. 1365–84.)

Owing to the widespread influence of the Clackmannanshire study, which led to synthetic phonics being widely adopted in Scottish schools, it was not possible to find a suitable comparison group in Scotland who had been taught by analytic phonics. Instead, a sample of classes in an English city was selected, who had been taught using a mixed approach including analytic phonics. The two samples are thus the 190 children aged 10 from the original Clackmannanshire study, who were taught primarily using synthetic phonics (which we shall call the 'synthetic phonics' group), and a comparable group of 203 children from schools in England, who were taught primarily using analytic phonics (the 'analytic phonics' group).

The reading test used was the Wide Range Achievement Test (WRAT test), while spelling was tested using the Schonell Spelling Test, as before. Both tests are standardised for chronological age. (The WRAT test has a higher upper age limit than the BAS test previously used.) Other tests were performed, notably reading comprehension, with similar results as for reading and spelling.

**Activity 22**   *Comparing reading abilities of 10-year-old children*

Table 36 shows the results of the WRAT reading test in the two groups of the Long Term study. As before, the reading ability variable has two categories: 'Not Higher' corresponds to reading age less than or equal to chronological age, while 'Higher' corresponds to reading age higher than chronological age. The age standardisation corrects for small age differences between children.

**Table 36**   Reading abilities at age 10

|                    | Standardised reading age |        |       |
|--------------------|:----------:|:------:|:-----:|
|                    | Not higher | Higher | Total |
| Analytic phonics   | 115        | 88     | 203   |
| Synthetic phonics  | 50         | 140    | 190   |
| Total              | 165        | 228    | 393   |

(a) Carry out the $\chi^2$ test of independence between teaching group and reading ability.

(b) What result would have been expected if there is no difference in the long term between the two teaching methods? What does this test suggest about the validity of this hypothesis?

In Activity 22, you found that the children in the synthetic phonics group did better at reading than those in the analytic phonics group, which suggests that the improvements in reading ability seen in the Clackmannanshire study are lasting. However, before reaching this conclusion, further issues have to be considered.

One issue is whether the two groups in the Long Term study are comparable with respect to other factors (besides teaching method) that might influence reading ability. For example, there is evidence that the socio-economic background of the child may have an impact on reading ability, with children from deprived backgrounds doing less well than children from advantaged backgrounds. Thus the observed association might have been induced by a difference in socio-economic backgrounds between the two groups, rather than by different teaching methods. This phenomenon, called **confounding**, is illustrated in Figure 6.

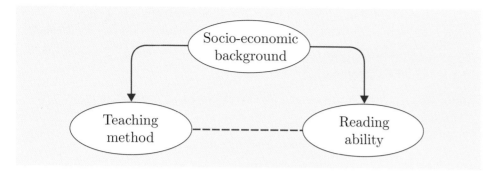

**Figure 6**   Confounding by socio-economic background

The arrows from 'Socio-economic background' to 'Teaching method' and from 'Socio-economic background' to 'Reading ability' indicate the presence of an association; the dashed line between 'Teaching method' and 'Reading ability' refers to an apparent association, which is actually induced by the other two: in this way, the true relationship (or lack of one) between 'Teaching method' and 'Reading ability' is *confounded* by socio-economic background.

Can such an effect explain the results observed in Table 36? This is the topic of Example 17.

**Example 17**   *The impact of socio-economic background on reading*

We want to know whether differences in socio-economic background can account for the pattern observed in Table 36. The children in the study were classified into two broad socio-economic groups, labelled 'Advantaged' and 'Disadvantaged'. One way to remove any confounding effect of socio-economic group is to do two analyses: one with children from advantaged backgrounds and another with children from disadvantaged backgrounds. Since the children in each group have similar socio-economic backgrounds, each of the two analyses should be free of any confounding effects due to this variable.

Table 37 shows the data for children from advantaged backgrounds only.

**Table 37**   Reading abilities of 10-year-old children from advantaged backgrounds

|  | Standardised reading age | | |
|  | Not higher | Higher | Total |
|---|---|---|---|
| Analytic phonics | 56 | 52 | 108 |
| Synthetic phonics | 21 | 82 | 103 |
| Total | 77 | 134 | 211 |

For these data, the test statistic is $\chi^2 = 22.520$. The Observed table is $2 \times 2$, so has one degree of freedom, and so CV5 = 3.841 and CV1 = 6.635. (You could check these numbers for yourself.) Since $22.520 \geq 6.635$, we reject the null hypothesis of independence at the 1% significance level.

Examination of Table 37 shows that, for children from advantaged backgrounds, better results are obtained in the synthetic phonics group.

What of children from disadvantaged backgrounds? Table 38 shows the data for children in this group.

**Table 38**   Reading abilities of 10-year-old children from disadvantaged backgrounds

|  | Standardised reading age | | |
|  | Not higher | Higher | Total |
| --- | --- | --- | --- |
| Analytic phonics | 59 | 36 | 95 |
| Synthetic phonics | 29 | 58 | 87 |
| Total | 88 | 94 | 182 |

In this case, $\chi^2 = 15.054$. The critical values are the same as before. Since $15.054 \geq 6.635$, the null hypothesis is rejected at the 1% significance level. And again, examination of Table 38 shows that children in the synthetic phonics group do better than those in the analytic phonics group.

By doing separate analyses for children from advantaged backgrounds and children from disadvantaged backgrounds, we have removed the effect of socio-economic background. In both groups, children taught by synthetic phonics appear to do better than children taught by analytic phonics. Thus, the observed relationship between teaching method and reading ability is not the result of confounding by socio-economic background.

*Confusion worse confounded*

Jones: 'Con-found it all! Somebody's taken my hat, and left this filthy, beastly, shabby old thing instead!'

Brown: 'A-I beg your pardon, but that happens to be my hat!'

Ruling out socio-economic background as a potential confounder is a big step towards being able to assert that synthetic phonics really does work better as a teaching method than analytic phonics. However, there are other confounders to think about – notably gender. Girls and boys may respond differently to different teaching methods, so it is important to study the possible confounding effect of gender in the Long Term study. This is the topic of Activity 23.

**Activity 23**   *Investigating the impact of gender on reading*

Table 39 shows the data in the Long Term Study for boys only.

**Table 39**   Reading abilities of 10-year-old boys

|  | Standardised reading age | | |
|  | Not higher | Higher | Total |
|---|---|---|---|
| Analytic phonics | 62 | 47 | 109 |
| Synthetic phonics | 20 | 86 | 106 |
| Total | 82 | 133 | 215 |

Table 40 shows the corresponding data for girls.

**Table 40**   Reading abilities of 10-year-old girls

|  | Standardised reading age | | |
|  | Not higher | Higher | Total |
|---|---|---|---|
| Analytic phonics | 53 | 41 | 94 |
| Synthetic phonics | 30 | 54 | 84 |
| Total | 83 | 95 | 178 |

(a)  Perform the $\chi^2$ test for independence in boys only using the data in Table 39.

(b)  Perform the $\chi^2$ test for independence in girls only using the data in Table 40.

(c)  Interpret your findings in terms of the presence or otherwise of confounding by gender in the Long Term study.

In Activity 23 you found that both boys' and girls' reading abilities are better in the synthetic phonics groups. In fact, you can say a little more than that. This is the topic of Example 18.

**Example 18**   *Comparing boys and girls*

Using $AP$ and $SP$ to denote membership of the analytic phonics and synthetic phonics groups respectively, we can calculate the conditional probabilities of achieving 'Higher' in the two groups, for boys and girls separately. Thus, for boys, using Table 39 we obtain:

$$P(\text{Higher}|AP) = \frac{47}{109} \simeq 0.431,$$
$$P(\text{Higher}|SP) = \frac{86}{106} \simeq 0.811.$$

Similarly for girls, from Table 40,

$$P(\text{Higher}|AP) = \frac{41}{94} \simeq 0.436,$$
$$P(\text{Higher}|SP) = \frac{54}{84} \simeq 0.643.$$

Thus, girls and boys in the analytic phonics groups perform much the same: the percentage whose reading age is higher than chronological age is about 43% for boys and 44% for girls.

Both boys and girls do better in the synthetic phonics groups: the percentages doing well are about 81% for boys and 64% for girls. But note that boys do particularly well. The improvement in ability is about 38% for boys $[(0.811 - 0.431) \times 100\%]$ compared to 21% for girls $[(0.643 - 0.436) \times 100\%]$.

Thus, it appears that, while both girls and boys do better when taught using synthetic rather than analytic phonics, boys respond particularly well to that method of teaching.

## 5.2 Reservations

We have spent a lot of time looking at data collected as part of the Clackmannanshire and Long Term studies. In this subsection, we critically consider the conclusions we drew from these studies.

'I have a Ph.D. and 20 years experience. But I'm a Statistician, so my conclusions will always be more qualified than I am.'

While both studies were carefully conducted, with due attention to comparability of groups, and outcomes assessed with well validated standardised tests, the children in each of the two studies were not actually selected at random from the populations of all children entering primary school, or of all 10-year-old primary school children. This, it must be said, is a feature of most studies, and does not in itself invalidate the results, but is something that must always be borne in mind. It is important to be on the lookout for any features of the data or of the study design that may suggest the individuals included or the measurements taken might be atypical in some way. In our case, there is nothing to suggest that the children and schools selected in these studies were atypical in any way.

*Despite the clear difference between the treated and control groups, something made him question the data.*

We now turn to reservations about our conclusions. There is one very important type of reservation that applies not only to the conclusions we have drawn in this unit but to all hypothesis tests. In a hypothesis test the procedure is to infer back from the sample to the appropriate population. The test used depends on the nature of the sample data and the question being posed, but in every case a similar procedure is adopted. We set up null and alternative hypotheses, find a test statistic from the sample data and compare it with critical values at the 5% and 1% significance levels to see if it lies in both, one or neither of the critical regions. If the test statistic lies in the critical region at the 1% significance level, then we reject the null hypothesis in favour of the alternative hypothesis at the 1% significance level and feel confident of our conclusion. If it lies in the critical region at the 5% significance level but not in that at the 1% significance level, we reject the null hypothesis at the 5% significance level and conclude that there is some evidence that the null hypothesis is false. If the test statistic lies in neither critical region then we conclude that there is insufficient evidence to reject the null hypothesis.

The use of a hypothesis test always carries with it the possibility of error, because we are using a sample to make inferences about a whole population. Even if the null hypothesis is true, random variation means that the test statistic obtained from a sample will sometimes unfortunately lie in the critical region. If we observed such a sample, we would reject the null hypothesis wrongly and so make an error. This type of error, where we reject the null hypothesis even though it is true, is known as a **type 1 error**.

Suppose that the null hypothesis ($H_0$) is true. If we use a significance level of 5%, there is a probability of 0.05 (5%) that the test statistic from a sample will lie in the critical region for the 5% significance level. That is, the probability of rejecting $H_0$ at the 5% significance level when $H_0$ is true is 0.05. Thus the probability of making a type 1 error is 0.05 if we use a 5% significance level. Similarly, if we reject $H_0$ at the 1% significance level, then when $H_0$ is true, the probability of making a type 1 error is 0.01. In general, the probability of making a type 1 error is given by the significance level at which $H_0$ is rejected.

It is also possible to make an error by *not* rejecting the null hypothesis when it is actually false. This is known as a **type 2 error**. It occurs when the particular sample we have picked has a test statistic that falls outside the critical region, even though the null hypothesis is false. Table 41 shows how the type 1 and type 2 errors relate to the null hypothesis.

**Table 41**   Type 1 and type 2 errors

|                     | $H_0$ true   | $H_0$ false  |
| ------------------- | ------------ | ------------ |
| $H_0$ not rejected  | Correct      | Type 2 error |
| $H_0$ rejected      | Type 1 error | Correct      |

You might be tempted to think that it is a good idea to make the probability of making a type 1 error as small as possible. However, for a given dataset, the two types of error are related, in that the smaller the probability of making a type 1 error, the larger the probability of making a type 2 error. So it is a matter of compromise, and the accepted procedure is to fix the probability of making a type 1 error.

The appropriate value to fix for this probability will vary with the situation. Most commonly, a probability of 0.05 of making a type 1 error is chosen. Sometimes, though, the action to be taken if the null hypothesis is rejected might be very expensive; in such a case, the probability of making a type 1 error might be fixed at 0.01 or even 0.001. As a result of such a choice, the probability of making a type 2 error would be larger.

It is not usually possible to quantify exactly the probability of making a type 2 error – the probability depends on the actual true form of the alternative hypothesis. Nevertheless, it is important to be aware of the possibility of making this type of error. The best way of reducing the probabilities of both types of error is to increase the sample size, by conducting a larger experiment.

**Activity 24**    *Which type of error?*

In each of the following scenarios, the 'truth' is first set out, then the result of a relevant hypothesis test is given. In each scenario, say whether a type 1 error, a type 2 error or no error has been made.

(a)  Reading ability after one year's primary school teaching is related to teaching method; the null hypothesis of independence was not rejected.

(b)  Reading ability at age 10 is related to teaching method; the null hypothesis of independence was rejected.

(c)  Spelling ability after one year's primary school teaching is unrelated to teaching method; the null hypothesis of independence was rejected.

(d)  Spelling ability at age 10 is unrelated to teaching method; the null hypothesis of independence was not rejected.

## Exercises on Section 5

Throughout this unit, we have focused on data about learning how to read. The methods we have described are, of course, universally applicable. The following two exercises are drawn from different fields of application.

**Exercise 10**    *Investigating gender differences in sandflies*

The data in Table 42 show the numbers of male and female sandflies caught in two light-traps, one set 3 feet and the other 35 feet above the ground. Is there any evidence to suggest that the variables height and gender are related?

**Table 42**    Trapped sandflies

|  | Height above ground | |
|---|---|---|
|  | 3 feet | 35 feet |
| Males | 173 | 125 |
| Females | 150 | 73 |

(Data source: Hand, D.J. et al. (1994) *A Handbook of Small Data Sets*, London, Chapman & Hall)

A sandfly takes off: how high will it fly?

(a)  Obtain the marginal totals, and set up the null and alternative hypotheses.

(b)  Carry out a $\chi^2$ test and state your conclusion.

(c)  What type of error might you have committed?

**Exercise 11**   *Investigating blood groups in Iraq*

Some data that were obtained from Iraq show the blood groups of samples of individuals from certain population groups.

**Table 43**   Blood groups in Iraq

| Population group | Blood group | | | | Total |
|---|---|---|---|---|---|
| | O | A | B | AB | |
| Kurd | 531 | 450 | 293 | 226 | 1500 |
| Arab | 174 | 150 | 133 | 36 | 493 |
| Other | 139 | 134 | 74 | 33 | 380 |
| Total | 844 | 734 | 500 | 295 | 2373 |

(Data source: Rohatgi, V.K. and Saleh, A.K. (2001) *An Introduction to Probability and Statistics*, 2nd edn, Wiley)

(a) Set up the null and alternative hypotheses appropriate to this contingency table.

(b) Carry out a $\chi^2$ test to investigate whether there is any relationship between blood group and ethnic group.

(c) State whether you may have made a type 1 or a type 2 error in your conclusion. If you conclude that there is a relationship, indicate the main differences in the blood group distributions for the different population groups.

# 6 Computer work: the $\chi^2$ test for contingency tables

In this section, you will learn how to use Minitab to perform the $\chi^2$ test on contingency tables, and how to enter data from contingency tables for analysis.

You should now turn to the Computer Book and work though Chapter 8.

## Summary

This unit has focused on the analysis of count data on two categorical variables, organised as a contingency table. Using data on the impact of different methods of teaching how to read, you learned to recognise contingency tables and calculate proportions from them.

The concepts of joint and conditional probabilities were described in terms of contingency tables. These types of probability are related by $P(A \text{ and } B) = P(A) \times P(B|A) = P(B) \times P(A|B)$, and they can be calculated from contingency tables. The addition rule for probabilities was extended to pairs of events that are not mutually exclusive. Also, the concept of statistical independence was related to conditional probabilities.

You learned how to formulate the null and alternative hypotheses for the $\chi^2$ test for contingency tables, how to calculate the $\chi^2$ test statistic, obtain the appropriate degrees of freedom, and obtain critical values for the test. You also learned how to interpret the results of the test in terms of the variables involved.

The distinction between association and causality was emphasised. The concept of confounding was described, along with how to investigate confounding by a third categorical variable. You were then introduced to type 1 and type 2 errors, and when they may occur.

Finally, you learned how to input contingency table data and how to carry out the $\chi^2$ test in Minitab.

# Learning outcomes

After working through this unit, you should be able to:

- recognise categorical data and categorical variables
- recognise a contingency table
- obtain the marginal totals of a contingency table
- calculate proportions from a contingency table
- state the dimensions of a contingency table
- recognise joint and conditional probabilities
- calculate joint and conditional probabilities from a contingency table
- state and use the relationship between joint and conditional probabilities
- state and use the general addition rule for probabilities
- express the independence of two events in terms of conditional probabilities
- carry out the $\chi^2$ test for contingency tables, taking account of the size of Expected values
- interpret a $\chi^2$ test in terms of the null and alternative hypotheses
- appreciate the distinction between association and causality
- investigate confounding by splitting a contingency table into several component tables and testing each table separately
- understand the concepts of type 1 and type 2 errors, and know when they may occur
- decide when to use the $\chi^2$ test for contingency tables
- input contingency tables into Minitab
- use Minitab to carry out the $\chi^2$ test.

# Solutions to activities

### Solution to Activity 1

The question starts with 'what is the best way'. So one aspect to clarify is which methods are to be compared, and then some criterion for measuring 'best' will be required. The rest of the question is 'teaching how to read', so we will need to specify exactly what is meant by 'how to read'.

### Solution to Activity 2

A sensible precaution is to test the children's reading ability before the different teaching methods are applied, in order to check that the children are starting from similar baselines. While differences in socio-economic or other factors between groups may still influence the effectiveness of the different teaching methods, demonstrating that the three groups are comparable from the start provides reassurance that the study is not fundamentally biased.

### Solution to Activity 3

(a) The proportion in the analytic phonics + PA group (denoted AP + PA) is

$$\frac{35}{78} \simeq 0.449,$$

or about 44.9%. In the synthetic phonics group (denoted SP), the proportion is

$$\frac{41}{117} \simeq 0.350,$$

or about 35.0%.

(b) The proportions in the three groups are: AP: 36%; AP + PA: 45%; and SP: 35%. The analytic phonics group and the synthetic phonics group are very similar, but the analytic phonics + PA group starts with perhaps a slight advantage.

## Solution to Activity 4

(a) The proportion of children in the analytic phonics group (AP) with reading age higher than chronological age is

$$\frac{36}{104} \simeq 0.346,$$

or about 34.6%. The proportion in the analytic phonics + PA group (AP + PA) is

$$\frac{24}{75} = 0.32,$$

or 32.0%. In the synthetic phonics group (SP), the proportion is

$$\frac{78}{113} \simeq 0.690,$$

or about 69.0%.

(b) The proportions in the three groups are: AP: 35%; AP + PA: 32%; and SP: 69%. The proportions of children whose reading age exceeds their chronological age remained steady, or perhaps even dropped, in the two groups receiving analytic phonics, whereas it increased dramatically (to 69% from 35% at the baseline test) in the synthetic phonics group.

(c) In order to interpret these results, it is necessary to find out whether the differences between the groups at the first follow-up test could be due to chance fluctuations. You might also want to know whether the impact of the synthetic phonics method is sustained over time (and indeed how the children performed on other tests).

## Solution to Activity 5

(a) This is not a contingency table. The column variable, chronological age at test, is not categorical. Note that it therefore makes no sense to consider whether the categories are mutually exclusive, as there are no categories. There are two columns, but these represent two different measurements on the same variable (age), rather than two categories of the same variable.

(b) This is not a contingency table. Although both variables are categorical and the entries are counts, the categories across the columns are not mutually exclusive: a child can have scored well both at the baseline test and at the first follow-up test.

## Solution to Activity 6

(a) The row variable has 3 categories and the column variable has 4 categories. Thus, $r = 3$ and $c = 4$, and so this is a $3 \times 4$ contingency table.

(b) Table 4 is $3 \times 2$. Swapping the rows and columns around would turn it into a $2 \times 3$ contingency table.

### Solution to Activity 7

(a)  This is the joint probability of events $R_2$ and $SP$.

$$P(R_2 \text{ and } SP) = \frac{\text{number of children with event } R_2 \text{ and event } SP}{\text{total number of children}}$$

$$= \frac{90}{268} \simeq 0.336.$$

(b)  This is the conditional probability of $R_2$, given $SP$.

$$P(R_2|SP) = \frac{\text{number of children experiencing } R_2 \text{ and } SP}{\text{number of children experiencing } SP}$$

$$= \frac{90}{105} \simeq 0.857.$$

(c)  This is the conditional probability of $AP+$, given $R_2$.

$$P(AP+|R_2) = \frac{\text{number of children experiencing } AP+ \text{ and } R_2}{\text{number of children experiencing } R_2}$$

$$= \frac{55}{223} \simeq 0.247.$$

### Solution to Activity 8

(a)  $P(R_2|SP)$

(b)  $P(R_2 \text{ and } SP)$

(c)  $P(SP|R_2)$

(d)  $P(R_2 \text{ and } SP)$

### Solution to Activity 9

For sixth form students, let 'Phys' denote the event 'studies physics', and 'Chem' the event 'studies chemistry'. Since 30% of sixth form students study physics, we have

$P(\text{Phys}) = 0.30.$

Also, among students who study physics, 80% also study chemistry, so

$P(\text{Chem}|\text{Phys}) = 0.80.$

Hence the proportion of students who study both physics and chemistry is

$$P(\text{Phys and Chem}) = P(\text{Phys}) \times P(\text{Chem}|\text{Phys})$$
$$= 0.30 \times 0.80$$
$$= 0.24.$$

Hence the probability that a student picked at random studies both physics and chemistry is 0.24.

## Solution to Activity 10

(a) By direct calculation, we have

$$P(S_0|AP+) = \frac{35}{78} \simeq 0.449,$$

and

$$P(S_0|SP) = \frac{47}{117} \simeq 0.402.$$

(b) We have, retaining more decimal places for intermediate results,

$$P(S_0 \text{ and } AP+) = \frac{35}{303} \simeq 0.1155$$

and

$$P(AP+) = \frac{78}{303} \simeq 0.2574.$$

So

$$P(S_0|AP+) \simeq \frac{0.1155}{0.2574} \simeq 0.449,$$

as obtained in part (a). Similarly,

$$P(S_0 \text{ and } SP) = \frac{47}{303} \simeq 0.1551$$

and

$$P(SP) = \frac{117}{303} \simeq 0.3861.$$

So

$$P(S_0|SP) \simeq \frac{0.1551}{0.3861} \simeq 0.402,$$

which is also equal to the corresponding value in part (a).

(c) The percentages spelling better than expected are therefore about 47.2% in the $AP$ group, 44.9% in the $AP+$ group, and 40.2% in the $SP$ group. The proportions are therefore broadly similar across groups, though a little lower in the $SP$ group.

## Solution to Activity 11

(a) Let 'Phys' denote the event 'studies physics', and 'Chem' the event 'studies chemistry'. Then

$$P(\text{Phys or Chem}) = P(\text{Phys}) + P(\text{Chem}) - P(\text{Phys and Chem})$$
$$= 0.30 + 0.32 - 0.24$$
$$= 0.38.$$

So 38% of sixth form students study physics or chemistry at this school.

(b) Let $R_0$ denote the event 'reading age at baseline higher than chronological age'. Then

$$P(R_0) = \frac{110}{291} \simeq 0.378, \quad P(R_1) = \frac{138}{291} \simeq 0.474,$$

and

$$P(R_0 \text{ and } R_1) = \frac{60}{291} \simeq 0.206.$$

So, using the general rule for adding probabilities,

$$P(R_0 \text{ or } R_1) = P(R_0) + P(R_1) - P(R_0 \text{ and } R_1)$$
$$\simeq 0.378 + 0.474 - 0.206$$
$$= 0.646.$$

(c)  Rearranging the general rule for adding probabilities,

$$P(A \text{ and } B) = P(A) + P(B) - P(A \text{ or } B).$$

Thus,

$$P(R_1 \text{ and } R_2) = P(R_1) + P(R_2) - P(R_1 \text{ or } R_2)$$
$$= 0.483 + 0.840 - 0.848$$
$$= 0.475.$$

So $263 \times 0.475 \simeq 125$ children did well on both tests.

(If unrounded values for $P(R_1)$, $P(R_2)$ and $P(R_1 \text{ or } R_2)$ are used instead of values correct to four decimal places as above, the product $263 \times P(R_1 \text{ and } R_2)$ is exactly equal to 125 and no '$\simeq$' is needed.)

## Solution to Activity 12

(a)  The probabilities are

$$P(S_2|AP) = \frac{85}{95} \simeq 0.895,$$

$$P(S_2|AP+) = \frac{59}{66} \simeq 0.894,$$

and

$$P(S_2|SP) = \frac{94}{104} \simeq 0.904.$$

(b)  Using the marginal totals,

$$P(S_2) = \frac{238}{265} \simeq 0.898.$$

(c)  The three conditional probabilities are very close to each other, and to the marginal probability $P(S_2)$, though not identical. This suggests that the original teaching group has little influence on the outcome of the second spelling test. It appears that the children in the two analytic phonics groups 'caught up' with those in the synthetic phonics group, after the synthetic phonics programme was extended to all children in the study.

## Solution to Activity 13

(a) We have $P(E \text{ and } M) = 0.48$, directly from Table 17.

The proportion studying English equals the proportion studying English and maths, plus the proportion studying English but not maths. So

$$P(E) = 0.48 + 0.32 = 0.80.$$

Similarly the proportion studying maths equals the proportion studying English and maths, plus the proportion studying maths but not English. So

$$P(M) = 0.48 + 0.12 = 0.60.$$

(b) We have

$$P(E|M) = \frac{P(E \text{ and } M)}{P(M)} = \frac{0.48}{0.60} = 0.80,$$

and

$$P(M|E) = \frac{P(M \text{ and } E)}{P(E)} = \frac{0.48}{0.80} = 0.60.$$

(c) Notice that $P(E|M) = P(E) = 0.80$, and $P(M|E) = P(M) = 0.60$. Thus, the events $E$ and $M$ are statistically independent.

## Solution to Activity 14

The hypotheses are:

$H_0$: Teaching method for children starting at primary school and reading ability at the baseline test are independent.

$H_1$: Teaching method for children starting at primary school and reading ability at the baseline test are not independent.

## Solution to Activity 15

(a) For the analytic phonics + PA group, the Expected values are:

Not higher: $75 \times \dfrac{154}{292} \simeq 39.5548$, Higher: $75 \times \dfrac{138}{292} \simeq 35.4452$.

(b) For the synthetic phonics group, the Expected values are:

Not higher: $113 \times \dfrac{154}{292} \simeq 59.5959$, Higher: $113 \times \dfrac{138}{292} \simeq 53.4041$.

## Solution to Activity 16

Start by copying the marginal totals from the Observed table to the Expected table. Then complete the Expected table by applying the equation in the highlighted box. We obtain, for example, the following Expected value for the 'Not higher' cell in the 'analytic phonics' group:

$$E = \frac{108 \times 188}{303} \simeq 67.0099.$$

The other Expected values are calculated in a similar manner.

|                        | Not higher | Higher  | Total |
|------------------------|------------|---------|-------|
| Analytic phonics       | 67.0099    | 40.9901 | 108   |
| Analytic phonics + PA  | 48.3960    | 29.6040 | 78    |
| Synthetic phonics      | 72.5941    | 44.4059 | 117   |
| Total                  | 188        | 115     | 303   |

The Expected values do indeed add up to the marginal totals from the Observed table.

## Solution to Activity 17

(a) The $\chi^2$ contribution for the cell corresponding to 'Not higher' in the analytic phonics group is

$$\chi^2 \text{ contribution} = \frac{(69 - 67.0099)^2}{67.0099}$$
$$\simeq 0.0591.$$

The other contributions are calculated in similar fashion, and are shown in the following table.

|                        | Not higher | Higher |
|------------------------|------------|--------|
| Analytic phonics       | 0.0591     | 0.0966 |
| Analytic phonics + PA  | 0.6016     | 0.9835 |
| Synthetic phonics      | 0.1598     | 0.2612 |

(b) The $\chi^2$ test statistic is:

$$\chi^2 = 0.0591 + 0.0966 + 0.6016 + 0.9835 + 0.1598 + 0.2612$$
$$= 2.1618$$
$$\simeq 2.162.$$

## Solution to Activity 18

We have $\chi^2 = 2.162 < 5.991$. Since $\chi^2 < \text{CV5}$, do not reject the null hypothesis. Thus, there is little evidence against the null hypothesis that reading ability in the baseline test is independent of the teaching group to which the children in the study were allocated.

## Solution to Activity 19

(a) Degrees of freedom $= 1$; CV5 $= 3.841$, CV1 $= 6.635$.

(b) Degrees of freedom $= 6$; CV5 $= 12.592$, CV1 $= 16.812$.

(c) Degrees of freedom $= 12$; CV5 $= 21.026$, CV1 $= 26.217$.

(d) Degrees of freedom $= 3$; CV5 $= 7.815$, CV1 $= 11.345$.

## Solution to Activity 20

(a) The hypotheses are as follows:

$H_0$: Teaching method originally allocated and reading ability at the second follow-up test are independent.

$H_1$: Teaching method originally allocated and reading ability at the second follow-up test are not independent.

(b) Copy marginal totals from the Observed table to the Expected table. Then the Expected value for the first cell is

$$\frac{\text{row total} \times \text{column total}}{\text{overall total}} = \frac{97 \times 45}{268} \simeq 16.2873.$$

The other values are obtained in the same manner, leading to the following Expected table:

|  | Not higher | Higher | Total |
|---|---|---|---|
| Analytic phonics | 16.2873 | 80.7127 | 97 |
| Analytic phonics + PA | 11.0821 | 54.9179 | 66 |
| Synthetic phonics | 17.6306 | 87.3694 | 105 |
| Total | 45 | 223 | 268 |

As a check on your calculations, the expected values within the table must add to the marginal totals (apart from unimportant rounding errors).

(c) The Residual table is found by subtracting the terms of the Expected table from those of the Observed table. For the first cell, we have

$$19 - 16.2873 = 2.7127.$$

The Residual table is:

|  | Not higher | Higher |
|---|---|---|
| Analytic phonics | 2.7127 | −2.7127 |
| Analytic phonics + PA | −0.0821 | 0.0821 |
| Synthetic phonics | −2.6306 | 2.6306 |

The $\chi^2$ contribution of the first cell is

$$\frac{\text{Residual}^2}{\text{Expected}} = \frac{2.7127^2}{16.2873} \simeq 0.4518.$$

The complete table of $\chi^2$ contributions is:

|  | Not higher | Higher |
|---|---|---|
| Analytic phonics | 0.4518 | 0.0912 |
| Analytic phonics + PA | 0.0006 | 0.0001 |
| Synthetic phonics | 0.3925 | 0.0792 |

(d) The $\chi^2$ test statistic is the sum of the six $\chi^2$ contributions:

$$\chi^2 = 0.4518 + 0.0912 + 0.0006 + 0.0001 + 0.3925 + 0.0792$$
$$\simeq 1.015.$$

The Observed table is a $3 \times 2$ table, so its degrees of freedom are $(3-1) \times (2-1) = 2$. Hence CV5 $= 5.991$ and CV1 $= 9.210$.

(e) Since $1.015 < 5.991$, we do not reject the null hypothesis that the teaching method originally allocated and reading ability at the second follow-up test are independent. In other words, there is little evidence that children's reading ability at this stage differs between the three teaching groups.

**Solution to Activity 21**

(a) The hypotheses are as follows:

$H_0$: Teaching method and ability in spelling/reading at the first follow-up test are independent.

$H_1$: Teaching method and ability in spelling/reading at the first follow-up test are not independent.

(b) Copy marginal totals from the Observed table to the Expected table. The Expected value for the first cell is

$$\frac{\text{row total} \times \text{column total}}{\text{overall total}} = \frac{179 \times 136}{292} \simeq 83.3699.$$

The other values are obtained in the same manner, leading to the following Expected table (with Observed marginal totals):

|  | Low/Low | Low/High | High/Low | High/High | Total |
|---|---|---|---|---|---|
| Any AP | 83.3699 | 17.7774 | 11.0342 | 66.8185 | 179 |
| Synthetic phonics | 52.6301 | 11.2226 | 6.9658 | 42.1815 | 113 |
| Total | 136 | 29 | 18 | 109 | 292 |

As a check on your calculations, the expected values within the table must add to the marginal totals (apart from unimportant rounding errors).

(c) The Residual table is found by subtracting the terms of the Expected table from those of the Observed table. For the first cell, we have

$$107 - 83.3699 = 23.6301.$$

The Residual table is:

|  | Low/Low | Low/High | High/Low | High/High |
|---|---|---|---|---|
| Any AP | 23.6301 | 4.2226 | 0.9658 | −28.8185 |
| Synthetic phonics | −23.6301 | −4.2226 | −0.9658 | 28.8185 |

The $\chi^2$ contribution of the first cell is

$$\frac{\text{Residual}^2}{\text{Expected}} = \frac{23.6301^2}{83.3699} \simeq 6.6976.$$

The complete table of $\chi^2$ contributions is:

|  | Low/Low | Low/High | High/Low | High/High |
|---|---|---|---|---|
| Any AP | 6.6976 | 1.0030 | 0.0845 | 12.4293 |
| Synthetic phonics | 10.6095 | 1.5888 | 0.1339 | 19.6889 |

(d) The $\chi^2$ test statistic is the sum of the eight $\chi^2$ contributions:

$$\begin{aligned} \chi^2 &= 6.6976 + 1.0030 + 0.0845 + 12.4293 + 10.6095 \\ &\quad + 1.5888 + 0.1339 + 19.6889 \\ &\simeq 52.236. \end{aligned}$$

The Observed table is a $2 \times 4$ table, so its degrees of freedom are $(2 - 1) \times (4 - 1) = 3$. Hence CV5 = 7.815 and CV1 = 11.345.

(e) Since $52.236 \geq 11.345$, we reject at the 1% significance level the null hypothesis that teaching method and spelling/reading ability at the first follow-up test are independent. There is strong evidence that children's spelling/reading ability differs between the two teaching groups.

(f) Examination of the $\chi^2$ contributions shows that the two biggest values are for the High/High ability category. The residuals corresponding to these cells are negative for 'any analytic phonics' and positive for synthetic phonics. Thus, the major departure from independence is due to children in the synthetic phonics group performing better in both spelling and reading than children in the 'any analytic phonics' group.

## Solution to Activity 22

(a) The Expected table (with Observed marginal totals) is:

|  | Not higher | Higher | Total |
|---|---|---|---|
| Analytic phonics | 85.2290 | 117.7710 | 203 |
| Synthetic phonics | 79.7710 | 110.2290 | 190 |
| Total | 165 | 228 | 393 |

The Residual table is:

|  | Not higher | Higher |
|---|---|---|
| Analytic phonics | 29.7710 | −29.7710 |
| Synthetic phonics | −29.7710 | 29.7710 |

The $\chi^2$ contributions table is:

|  | Not higher | Higher |
|---|---|---|
| Analytic phonics | 10.3992 | 7.5257 |
| Synthetic phonics | 11.1107 | 8.0406 |

The $\chi^2$ test statistic is:

$$\chi^2 = 10.3992 + 7.5257 + 11.1107 + 8.0406 \simeq 37.076.$$

The Observed table has $(2-1) \times (2-1) = 1$ degree of freedom, so $CV5 = 3.841$ and $CV1 = 6.635$. Since $37.076 \geq 6.635$, we reject the null hypothesis at the 1% significance level. Thus, there is strong evidence that reading ability varies with teaching method.

(b) Examination of the Observed table (you could also look at the $\chi^2$ contributions and residuals, but for a $2 \times 2$ table it's easier to just look at the data) shows that the synthetic phonics group have done better than the analytic phonics group. If the impact of synthetic phonics teaching was short-lived, we would expect to see no difference between the groups. Thus, on the face of it, it seems that the data do not support this hypothesis. Thus, synthetic phonics teaching appears to confer a lasting advantage.

## Solution to Activity 23

(a) The Expected table (with Observed marginals) is:

|  | Not higher | Higher | Total |
|---|---|---|---|
| Analytic phonics | 41.5721 | 67.4279 | 109 |
| Synthetic phonics | 40.4279 | 65.5721 | 106 |
| Total | 82 | 133 | 215 |

The Residual table is:

|  | Not higher | Higher |
|---|---|---|
| Analytic phonics | 20.4279 | −20.4279 |
| Synthetic phonics | −20.4279 | 20.4279 |

The $\chi^2$ contributions table is:

|  | Not higher | Higher |
|---|---|---|
| Analytic phonics | 10.0380 | 6.1888 |
| Synthetic phonics | 10.3221 | 6.3640 |

The $\chi^2$ test statistic is 32.913. This is greater than 6.635, the value of CV1 for one degree of freedom. Hence we reject the null hypothesis that boys' reading ability is independent of teaching group. Examination of the Observed table shows that boys in the synthetic phonics group perform better than boys in the analytic phonics group.

(b) The Expected table (with Observed marginals) is:

|  | Not higher | Higher | Total |
|---|---|---|---|
| Analytic phonics | 43.8315 | 50.1685 | 94 |
| Synthetic phonics | 39.1685 | 44.8315 | 84 |
| Total | 83 | 95 | 178 |

The Residual table is:

|  | Not higher | Higher |
|---|---|---|
| Analytic phonics | 9.1685 | −9.1685 |
| Synthetic phonics | −9.1685 | 9.1685 |

The $\chi^2$ contributions table is:

|  | Not higher | Higher |
|---|---|---|
| Analytic phonics | 1.9178 | 1.6756 |
| Synthetic phonics | 2.1461 | 1.8751 |

The $\chi^2$ test statistic is 7.615. This is greater than 6.635, the value of CV1 for one degree of freedom. Hence we reject the null hypothesis that girls' reading ability is independent of teaching group. Examination of the Observed table shows that girls in the synthetic phonics group perform better than girls in the analytic phonics group.

(c) Reading ability is better in the synthetic phonics group than in the analytic phonics group for both boys and girls. Thus, gender is not a confounder for the association between reading ability and teaching method.

## Solution to Activity 24

(a) The null hypothesis of independence is false, but was not rejected: a type 2 error was made.

(b) The null hypothesis of independence is false, and was rejected: no error was made.

(c) The null hypothesis of independence is true, but was rejected: a type 1 error was made.

(d) The null hypothesis is true, and was not rejected: no error was made.

# Solutions to exercises

### Solution to Exercise 1

One way to look at this would be to do separate analyses for boys and girls within each teaching method group, to see if there are differences between boys and girls, and whether those differences vary between teaching methods.

### Solution to Exercise 2

(a)  The overall proportion of girls is

$$\frac{146}{304} \simeq 0.480.$$

Hence the percentage of girls is 48.0% (to one decimal place).

(b)  The proportion of boys in the analytic phonics group is

$$\frac{58}{109} \simeq 0.532.$$

In the analytic phonics + PA group it is

$$\frac{39}{78} = 0.5,$$

while in the synthetic phonics group it is

$$\frac{61}{117} \simeq 0.521.$$

(c)  The proportions of boys in the three groups are similar. (You would not expect them to be exactly equal, owing to random fluctuations.)

### Solution to Exercise 3

(a)  Table 10 is a contingency table. The variables are categorical: the row variable has two mutually exclusive categories, 'analytic phonics with or without PA' and 'synthetic phonics', and gender also has two mutually exclusive categories (for our purposes, anyway). Finally, the entries are counts.

Table 11 is not a contingency table: as made clear in its caption, it represents percentages, so the entries are not counts. The percentages have been rounded to the nearest whole number so they might *look* like counts, but they are not (and they add up to 100% for each row).

(b)  Each of the variables in Table 10 has two categories, so the table is a $2 \times 2$ table. Table 11 is not a contingency table, but if you thought it was and calculated its dimension as if it were a contingency table, you'd most likely have observed that it has 3 rows and 2 columns, and so classified it as being a $3 \times 2$ table.

## Solution to Exercise 4

(a) $P(G|AP) = \dfrac{51}{109} \simeq 0.468$.

(b) $P(AP+) = \dfrac{78}{304} \simeq 0.257$.

(c) $P(SP|B) = \dfrac{61}{158} \simeq 0.386$.

(d) $P(B \text{ and } AP+) = \dfrac{39}{304} \simeq 0.128$.

(e) This probability is
$$P(G|SP) = \frac{56}{117} \simeq 0.479.$$

(f) This probability is
$$P(AP|B) = \frac{58}{158} \simeq 0.367.$$

## Solution to Exercise 5

(a) We have
$$P(R_2|S_2) = \frac{P(R_2 \text{ and } S_2)}{P(S_2)}.$$

Now, retaining more decimal places for intermediate results,
$$P(S_2) = \frac{237}{264} \simeq 0.8977,$$
and
$$P(R_2 \text{ and } S_2) = \frac{214}{264} \simeq 0.8106.$$
So
$$P(R_2|S_2) \simeq \frac{0.8106}{0.8977} \simeq 0.903.$$

(b) This probability is $P(S_2|R_2)$. Thus, similarly to part (a),
$$P(S_2|R_2) = \frac{P(S_2 \text{ and } R_2)}{P(R_2)}.$$

Now
$$P(R_2) = \frac{220}{264} \simeq 0.8333,$$
and (from the solution to part (a))
$$P(S_2 \text{ and } R_2) \simeq 0.8106.$$
So
$$P(S_2|R_2) \simeq \frac{0.8106}{0.8333} \simeq 0.973.$$

(c) Applying the general addition rule,

$$P(R_2 \text{ or } S_2) = P(R_2) + P(S_2) - P(R_2 \text{ and } S_2).$$

From parts (a) and (b), $P(R_2) \simeq 0.8333$, $P(S_2) \simeq 0.8977$, and $P(R_2 \text{ and } S_2) \simeq 0.8106$. So

$$P(R_2 \text{ or } S_2) \simeq 0.8333 + 0.8977 - 0.8106 \simeq 0.920.$$

## Solution to Exercise 6

(a) The row and column variables are categorical. The variables each have mutually exclusive categories, since a child must be either 'Low' or 'High' on each test. Finally, the entries are counts. Hence Table 19 is a contingency table.

(b) We have

$$P(\text{Reading High|Spelling Low}) = \frac{6}{27} \simeq 0.222,$$

and

$$P(\text{Reading High}) = \frac{220}{264} \simeq 0.833.$$

(c) The two probabilities are very different. This suggests that spelling and reading ability are not independent. However, some difference is to be expected owing to random fluctuations. We need to know whether the observed difference could plausibly have arisen by chance.

## Solution to Exercise 7

(a) The hypotheses are as follows:

$H_0$: Teaching method and spelling ability at the first follow-up test are independent.

$H_1$: Teaching method and spelling ability at the first follow-up test are not independent.

(b) Copy marginal totals from the Observed table to the Expected table. The Expected value for the first cell is

$$\frac{\text{row total} \times \text{column total}}{\text{overall total}} = \frac{104 \times 165}{292} \simeq 58.7671.$$

The other values are obtained in the same manner, leading to the following Expected table:

|  | Not higher | Higher | Total |
|---|---|---|---|
| Analytic phonics | 58.7671 | 45.2329 | 104 |
| Analytic phonics + PA | 42.3801 | 32.6199 | 75 |
| Synthetic phonics | 63.8527 | 49.1473 | 113 |
| Total | 165 | 127 | 292 |

(To check your calculations, add up the expected values in each column and in each row. These should give the marginal totals of the table, apart from unimportant rounding errors.)

(c) The Residual table is found by subtracting the terms of the Expected table from those of the Observed table. For the first cell, we have

$$79 - 58.7671 = 20.2329.$$

The Residual table is:

|  | Not higher | Higher |
|---|---|---|
| Analytic phonics | 20.2329 | −20.2329 |
| Analytic phonics + PA | 7.6199 | −7.6199 |
| Synthetic phonics | −27.8527 | 27.8527 |

The $\chi^2$ contribution of the first cell is

$$\frac{\text{Residual}^2}{\text{Expected}} = \frac{20.2329^2}{58.7671} \simeq 6.9660.$$

The complete table of $\chi^2$ contributions is:

|  | Not higher | Higher |
|---|---|---|
| Analytic phonics | 6.9660 | 9.0503 |
| Analytic phonics + PA | 1.3701 | 1.7800 |
| Synthetic phonics | 12.1494 | 15.7846 |

(d) The $\chi^2$ test statistic is the sum of the six $\chi^2$ contributions:

$$\chi^2 = 6.9660 + 9.0503 + 1.3701 + 1.7800 + 12.1494 + 15.7846$$
$$\simeq 47.100.$$

The Observed table is a $3 \times 2$ table, so its degrees of freedom are $(3-1) \times (2-1) = 2$. Hence CV5 = 5.991 and CV1 = 9.210.

(e) Since $47.100 \geq 9.210$, we reject at the 1% significance level the null hypothesis that teaching method and spelling ability at the first follow-up test are independent. There is strong evidence that children's spelling ability at this stage differs between the three teaching groups.

(f) Examination of the table of $\chi^2$ contributions shows that the largest values are for the synthetic phonics group. The corresponding residuals are negative for 'Not higher' and positive for 'Higher'. Thus, the major departure from independence comes from children in the synthetic phonics group performing better in the spelling test than would be expected under the assumption of independence.

## Solution to Exercise 8

(a) The hypotheses are as follows:

$H_0$: Teaching method originally allocated and spelling ability at the second follow-up test are independent.

$H_1$: Teaching method originally allocated and spelling ability at the second follow-up test are not independent.

(b) Copy marginal totals from the Observed table to the Expected table. The Expected value for the first cell is

$$\frac{\text{row total} \times \text{column total}}{\text{overall total}} = \frac{95 \times 27}{265} \simeq 9.6792.$$

The other values are obtained in the same manner, leading to the following Expected table:

|  | Not higher | Higher | Total |
|---|---|---|---|
| Analytic phonics | 9.6792 | 85.3208 | 95 |
| Analytic phonics + PA | 6.7245 | 59.2755 | 66 |
| Synthetic phonics | 10.5962 | 93.4038 | 104 |
| Total | 27 | 238 | 265 |

As a check on your calculations, the expected values within the table must add to the marginal totals (ignoring unimportant rounding errors).

(c) The Residual table is found by subtracting the terms of the Expected table from those of the Observed table. For the first cell, we have

$$10 - 9.6792 = 0.3208.$$

The Residual table is:

|  | Not higher | Higher |
|---|---|---|
| Analytic phonics | 0.3208 | −0.3208 |
| Analytic phonics + PA | 0.2755 | −0.2755 |
| Synthetic phonics | −0.5962 | 0.5962 |

The $\chi^2$ contribution of the first cell is

$$\frac{\text{Residual}^2}{\text{Expected}} = \frac{0.3208^2}{9.6792} \simeq 0.0106.$$

The complete table of $\chi^2$ contributions is:

|  | Not higher | Higher |
|---|---|---|
| Analytic phonics | 0.0106 | 0.0012 |
| Analytic phonics + PA | 0.0113 | 0.0013 |
| Synthetic phonics | 0.0335 | 0.0038 |

(d) The $\chi^2$ test statistic is the sum of the six $\chi^2$ contributions:

$$\chi^2 = 0.0106 + 0.0012 + 0.0113 + 0.0013 + 0.0335 + 0.0038$$
$$\simeq 0.062.$$

The Observed table is a $3 \times 2$ table, so its degrees of freedom are $(3-1) \times (2-1) = 2$. Hence CV5 = 5.991 and CV1 = 9.210.

(e) Since $0.062 < 5.991$, we do not reject the null hypothesis that teaching method and spelling ability at the second follow-up test are independent. There is little evidence that children's spelling ability at this stage is related to the groups to which they were originally allocated.

## Solution to Exercise 9

(a) The hypotheses are as follows:

$H_0$: Teaching method and ability in spelling/reading at the first follow-up test are independent.

$H_1$: Teaching method and ability in spelling/reading at the first follow-up test are not independent.

(b) Copy marginal totals from the Observed table to the Expected table. The Expected value for the first cell is

$$\frac{\text{row total} \times \text{column total}}{\text{overall total}} = \frac{104 \times 136}{292} \simeq 48.4384.$$

The other values are obtained in the same manner, leading to the following Expected table:

|  | Low/Low | L/H or H/L | High/High | Total |
|---|---|---|---|---|
| Analytic phonics | 48.4384 | 16.7397 | 38.8219 | 104 |
| Analytic phonics + PA | 34.9315 | 12.0719 | 27.9966 | 75 |
| Synthetic phonics | 52.6301 | 18.1884 | 42.1815 | 113 |
| Total | 136 | 47 | 109 | 292 |

As a check on your calculations, the expected values within the table must add to the marginal totals (ignoring unimportant rounding errors).

(c) The Residual table is found by subtracting the terms of the Expected table from those of the Observed table. For the first cell, we have

$$65 - 48.4384 = 16.5616.$$

The Residual table is:

|  | Low/Low | L/H or H/L | High/High |
|---|---|---|---|
| Analytic phonics | 16.5616 | 0.2603 | −16.8219 |
| Analytic phonics + PA | 7.0685 | 4.9281 | −11.9966 |
| Synthetic phonics | −23.6301 | −5.1884 | 28.8185 |

The $\chi^2$ contribution of the first cell is

$$\frac{\text{Residual}^2}{\text{Expected}} = \frac{16.5616^2}{48.4384} \simeq 5.6626.$$

The complete table of $\chi^2$ contributions is:

|  | Low/Low | L/H or H/L | High/High |
|---|---|---|---|
| Analytic phonics | 5.6626 | 0.0040 | 7.2891 |
| Analytic phonics + PA | 1.4303 | 2.0118 | 5.1406 |
| Synthetic phonics | 10.6095 | 1.4800 | 19.6889 |

(d) The $\chi^2$ test statistic is the sum of the nine $\chi^2$ contributions:

$$\chi^2 = 5.6626 + 0.0040 + 7.2891 + 1.4303 + 2.0118 + 5.1406$$
$$+ 10.6095 + 1.4800 + 19.6889$$
$$\simeq 53.317.$$

The Observed table is a $3 \times 3$ table, so its degrees of freedom are $(3-1) \times (3-1) = 4$. Hence CV5 = 9.488 and CV1 = 13.277.

(e) Since $53.317 \geq 13.277$, we reject at the 1% significance level the null hypothesis that teaching method and spelling/reading ability at the first follow-up test are independent. There is strong evidence that children's spelling/reading ability differs between the two teaching groups.

(f) Examination of the $\chi^2$ contributions shows that the two biggest values are for the High/High and Low/Low ability categories within the synthetic phonics group. The residuals corresponding to these cells are negative for Low/Low and positive for High/High. Thus, the major departure from independence is due to children in the synthetic phonics group performing better in both spelling and reading than children in the other teaching method groups.

## Solution to Exercise 10

(a) The contingency table with marginal totals is:

|         | Height above ground | | |
|---------|--------|---------|-------|
|         | 3 feet | 35 feet | Total |
| Males   | 173    | 125     | 298   |
| Females | 150    | 73      | 223   |
| Total   | 323    | 198     | 521   |

The hypotheses are as follows:

$H_0$: The gender of sandflies caught in light-traps is independent of the height above the ground of the traps.

$H_1$: The gender of sandflies caught in light-traps is not independent of the height above the ground of the traps.

(b) The Expected table (with Observed marginal totals) is:

|         | 3 feet   | 35 feet  | Total |
|---------|----------|----------|-------|
| Males   | 184.7486 | 113.2514 | 298   |
| Females | 138.2514 | 84.7486  | 223   |
| Total   | 323      | 198      | 521   |

Note that all Expected values are greater than or equal to 5, so the test can proceed.

The Residual table is:

|         | 3 feet   | 35 feet  |
|---------|----------|----------|
| Males   | −11.7486 | 11.7486  |
| Females | 11.7486  | −11.7486 |

The $\chi^2$ contributions table is:

|         | 3 feet  | 35 feet |
|---------|---------|---------|
| Males   | 0.7471  | 1.2188  |
| Females | 0.9984  | 1.6287  |

The $\chi^2$ test statistic is 4.593. This is greater than 3.841, the value of CV5 for one degree of freedom, but not greater than CV1, which is 6.635. Hence we reject the null hypothesis at the 5% significance level, but not at the 1% significance level.

We conclude that there is some evidence that the gender of sandflies caught in light-traps and the height of traps above the ground are not independent.

None of the terms in the $\chi^2$ contributions table are large. We note that the number of males caught in traps 35 feet above ground level and the number of females caught in traps 3 feet above ground level are higher than the corresponding Expected values. In fact 58% $(173/298 \times 100\%)$ of males were caught 35 feet above ground level, compared to only 33% of females. This suggests that male sandflies are more likely to fly high than females.

(c) Since the null hypothesis has been rejected, a type 1 error might have been committed.

## Solution to Exercise 11

(a) The null and alternative hypotheses are as follows.

$H_0$: The blood group of an individual in Iraq is independent of which population group he or she belongs to.

$H_1$: The blood group of an individual in Iraq is not independent of which population group he or she belongs to.

(b) The Expected table is as follows, with Observed marginal totals.

|       | O        | A        | B        | AB       | Total |
|-------|----------|----------|----------|----------|-------|
| Kurd  | 533.5019 | 463.9697 | 316.0556 | 186.4728 | 1500  |
| Arab  | 175.3443 | 152.4914 | 103.8769 | 61.2874  | 493   |
| Other | 135.1538 | 117.5390 | 80.0674  | 47.2398  | 380   |
| Total | 844      | 734      | 500      | 295      | 2373  |

All Expected values are greater than or equal to 5, so the test can proceed.

The Residual table is as follows:

|       | O        | A         | B         | AB        |
|-------|----------|-----------|-----------|-----------|
| Kurd  | −2.5019  | −13.9697  | −23.0556  | 39.5272   |
| Arab  | −1.3443  | −2.4914   | 29.1231   | −25.2874  |
| Other | 3.8462   | 16.4610   | −6.0674   | −14.2398  |

The $\chi^2$ contributions tables is:

|       | O      | A      | B      | AB      |
|-------|--------|--------|--------|---------|
| Kurd  | 0.0117 | 0.4206 | 1.6819 | 8.3787  |
| Arab  | 0.0103 | 0.0407 | 8.1650 | 10.4337 |
| Other | 0.1095 | 2.3053 | 0.4598 | 4.2924  |

The $\chi^2$ test statistic is $\chi^2 = 36.310$.

The degrees of freedom are $(3 - 1) \times (4 - 1) = 6$, so CV5 = 12.592 and CV1 = 16.812. Since $36.310 \geq 16.812$, we reject $H_0$ at the 1% significance level. There is strong evidence that blood group is not independent of population group for people in Iraq.

(c)  We might have committed a type 1 error, as we rejected the null hypothesis.

The highest $\chi^2$ terms are 8.3787, 8.1650 and 10.4337, which come from the Kurd and Arab populations. Of the Kurds, 15% are of group AB compared to only 7% of Arabs. Arabs have a much higher percentage (27%) of group B than the other population groups.

# Acknowledgements

Grateful acknowledgement is made to the following sources:

Cover image: Minxlj/www.flickr.com/photos/minxlj/422472167/. This file is licensed under the Creative Commons Attribution-Non commercial-No Derivatives Licence http://creativecommons.org/licenses/by-nc-nd/3.0/

Figure 1 © Penguin Group

Figure 2 TUBS. http://en.wikipedia.org/wiki/File:Clackmannanshire_in_Scotland.svg. This file is licensed under the Creative Commons Attribution-Share Alike 3.0 Unported license.

Exercises on Section 1, cartoon: Randy Glasbergen / www.glasbergen.com

Subsection 2.1 photo ('Learning how to read'), Monkey Business Images / Dreamstime

Subsection 2.2 photo ('Children reading'), Cliff Parnell / www.istockphoto.com

Subsection 3.1 cartoon (reading at a 3rd grade level), www.cartoonstock.com

Subsection 3.2 photo ('In the classroom'), daaronj / www.istockphoto.com

Subsection 5.2 cartoon (20 years experience), www.causeweb.org

Subsection 5.2 cartoon (question the data), www.causeweb.org

Exercises on Section 5, photo of sandfly: Commander Applebery / Flickr.com. This file is licensed under the Creative Commons Attribution-Share Alike Licence http://creativecommons.org/licenses/by-sa/3.0/

Every effort has been made to contact copyright holders. If any have been inadvertently overlooked the publishers will be pleased to make the necessary arrangements at the first opportunity.

# Unit 9

# Comparing schools

# Introduction

In Books 3 and 4 so far, we have looked at questions related to education. In Unit 6 we looked at the question: *How often do pupils truant?* The theme of Unit 7 was the question: *What factors affect a child's reading ability?* The focus of Unit 8 was: *What is the best way of teaching how to read?* We have looked at various statistical techniques to help answer these questions. For example, in Unit 6 you used the sign test to investigate truancy rates. And in Unit 7 you used a $z$-test to test hypotheses about the reading scores of seven- and eight-year-old British children. In this unit, we will consider the following question:

> *How good is a school?*

This is a question that is of interest to politicians as well as parents and teachers.

In the UK general election of 2010, the three main political parties all made reference to the quality of schools in their manifestos. Quotes include:

'Raise standards in schools' – Conservatives

'Every school a good school' – Labour

'Ensure that every neighbourhood is served by an excellent local school or college' – Liberal Democrats

Charles Dickens's character Nicholas Nickleby tries to improve the standard of Dotheboys Hall School

In Section 1 we will consider how to measure the quality of a school. We will narrow the definition of school quality to something that can be objectively measured, and present some data. Section 2 introduces the correlation coefficient – a measure of the strength of the relationship between two variables. In Section 3 you will learn some more about the properties of the correlation coefficient. In Section 4 you will learn how to construct intervals for means that complement one-sample $z$-tests and two-sample $z$-tests – intervals that are known as *confidence intervals*. In Section 5 you will learn about making two types of intervals for predictions from a regression line, intervals that are known as *confidence intervals for the mean response* and *prediction intervals*. Finally, Section 6 will return to the measurement of the quality of a school.

Note that you will be guided to the Computer Book in Subsections 2.4 and 5.3. Similarly to previous units, it is better if you do the work at these points in the text, although you can leave it until later if you prefer.

# 1 Measuring school quality

The theme of this unit is the question: *How good is a school?* The problem with this question is one of definition. What makes a school good? How can we measure a school's quality? So, to make progress, it is necessary to clarify what we mean by a 'good school'.

## 1.1 Clarifying the question

In order to judge the quality of a school it is necessary to know what makes some good and others not-so-good.

**Activity 1**  *Thinking about the definition*

Spend a few minutes thinking about what makes a school good, and list some of your thoughts.

For this unit we will just consider one measure of school quality, the academic achievement of its students.

**Activity 2**  *Measuring academic achievement*

Think about the ways in which the academic ability of a student can be measured.

In this unit we will focus on measuring the quality of secondary schools in England. In particular we will focus on the academic achievement of students at the end of one phase of their education – the end of what is known as Key Stage 4.

## Key Stages

In England, many state schools must follow a curriculum laid down by the government – the 'National Curriculum'. The National Curriculum is broken down into a number of 'Key Stages', each stage corresponding to a number of year groups at school.

Key Stages

|  | Ages | School years |
|---|---|---|
| Key Stage 1 | 5 to 7 | 1 and 2 |
| Key Stage 2 | 7 to 11 | 3 to 6 |
| Key Stage 3 | 11 to 14 | 7 to 9 |
| Key Stage 4 | 14 to 16 | 10 and 11 |

(Source: Gov.uk (2013) 'The national curriculum')

In Wales and Northern Ireland, the curriculum is also broken up into Key Stages. Although the details vary, in all three countries the end of Key Stage 2 corresponds to the end of primary education and the end of Key Stage 4 corresponds to the end of compulsory education at age 16.

The academic achievement of students when they finish Key Stage 4 can be measured by looking at how many, and which, national qualifications they are awarded at that point in their education. In particular, this can be done by considering one set of qualifications that students in England generally finish at the end of Key Stage 4 – GCSEs.

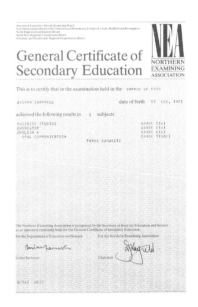

### GCSE – General Certificate of Secondary Education

GCSEs (General Certificates of Secondary Education) are qualifications that are generally awarded to students at the end of Key Stage 4 in England, Wales and Northern Ireland. (Students in Scotland usually take Standard Grades instead of GCSEs.) The qualification was first awarded in 1988 and replaced GCE 'O'-Levels and CSEs.

GCSE grades of pass (in order from highest to lowest) are as follows: A*, A, B, C, D, E, F and G.

Grades A* to C correspond to Level 2 qualifications on the National Qualifications Framework for England and Northern Ireland and the Credit and Qualifications Framework for Wales – the same as Credit Standard Grades in Scotland and, at the time the qualification was introduced, the same as GCE 'O' levels at grades A to C and CSEs at grade 1.

Grades D to G correspond to Level 1 qualifications on the same frameworks – the same as General Standard Grades in Scotland and, at the time the qualifications were introduced, the same as CSEs at grades 2 to 5.

As students at a secondary school generally take a variety of GCSEs, both in terms of numbers and subjects, it is necessary to combine the students' individual results in some way to get a measure of overall academic achievement by students at the school. One such measure that is commonly used at the time of writing is as follows.

### GCSE headline figure, $P_{KS4}$

A measure of a secondary school's quality will be taken to be the percentage of students ending Key Stage 4 who achieve at least five grade A* to C GCSEs, including English and Mathematics.

This percentage will be denoted as $P_{KS4}$ and referred to as a school's **GCSE headline figure**.

So, using $P_{KS4}$ it is possible to measure a secondary school's quality. (Assuming that the information is available. It is not published for all English secondary schools.) This provides a numerical answer to the question: *How good is a school?* However, there is a problem: the numerical answer needs to be put into context.

## Activity 3   *Is a local secondary school good enough?*

Suppose an English secondary school has a GCSE headline figure of 64%. Is this school good?

The threshold for a 'good' secondary school could be an absolute one. For example, the government could decide that the $P_{KS4}$ in any good school should be at least 50%. But the threshold can be also set in a relative sense. For example, a secondary school might be classified as 'good' if its $P_{KS4}$ equals or exceeds the median. To decide such relative thresholds, it is important to have a feel for the range of $P_{KS4}$ that usually occurs. For this we need some data.

### A minimum standard for English secondary schools

In a White Paper for 2010, the UK government set out a 'floor' standard for English secondary schools – that is, a minimum standard that every secondary school is expected to achieve. The White Paper (paragraph 6.26) states that:

> a school will be below the floor if fewer than 35 per cent of pupils achieve the 'basics' standard of 5 A*–C grade GCSEs including English and Mathematics, and fewer pupils make good progress between key stage two and key stage four than the national average.

(Source: Department for Education (2010) *The Importance of Teaching: Schools White Paper*, London: The Stationery Office)

## 1.2   The data to be used

In Subsection 1.1 the quality of a secondary school was defined to be $P_{KS4}$, the percentage of students ending Key Stage 4 who achieve at least five grade A* to C GCSEs, including English and Mathematics. It was noted that it is important to be able to put a value of $P_{KS4}$ into context. We will do this by considering how $P_{KS4}$ varies for a particular group of secondary schools.

The sample we will use is a random sample of 100 English state secondary schools. Each of the schools chosen had at least 100 students ending Key Stage 4 in 2011. Furthermore, only 'non-selective' schools were chosen – that is, schools where the admissions policy does not include selection on the basis of ability.

At the time of writing, data about all state secondary schools in England are released annually by the Department for Education. These data include $P_{KS4}$, and so information is known about the entire population for 2011. However, some of the questions we will look at in this unit will be relevant to other years. This might include future years. So, in this sense, the values of $P_{KS4}$ are not known for the whole population.

Histograms were introduced in Subsection 1.5 of the Computer Book.

A histogram of $P_{KS4}$ for the 100 schools is shown in Figure 1.

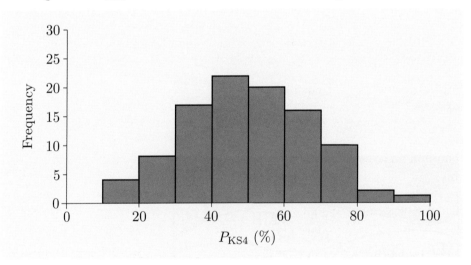

**Figure 1**   Histogram of $P_{KS4}$ in 100 schools

**Activity 4**   *Describing the distribution*

Use the histogram given in Figure 1 to describe the distribution of $P_{KS4}$ in our sample of 100 secondary schools.

## Activity 5   *Determining 'good enough' schools*

The heights of each of the bars in Figure 1 are given in Table 1.

**Table 1**   $P_{KS4}$ in 100 schools

| $P_{KS4}$ | Number of schools |
|---|---|
| 0% to just under 10% | 0 |
| 10% to just under 20% | 4 |
| 20% to just under 30% | 8 |
| 30% to just under 40% | 17 |
| 40% to just under 50% | 22 |
| 50% to just under 60% | 20 |
| 60% to just under 70% | 16 |
| 70% to just under 80% | 10 |
| 80% to just under 90% | 2 |
| 90% to just under 100% | 1 |

Using this information, how many schools in our sample would be deemed to be not good enough if the following criteria for 'good' were used?

(a)  $P_{KS4} \geq 50\%$

(b)  $P_{KS4} \geq 30\%$

(c)  $P_{KS4} \geq 90\%$

So, as Figure 1 shows, the GCSE headline figure varies considerably in our sample of 100 secondary schools. Such information allows the 'better' schools to be identified. What then? Individual parents might use this information when deciding the school they wish their child to attend. Those in charge of education, locally or nationally, might also use this information to decide which schools are not performing well enough and hence need to improve. But it does not suggest how such schools might achieve such improvement. For this a second question is important: *What factors influence the quality of a school?*

Some potential factors just split schools into two groups. For example:

- selective or non-selective
- single sex or co-educational
- in London or in the rest of England.

In Unit 7, you met a method for investigating such potential factors – the two-sample $z$-test. Recall that the two-sample $z$-test works by comparing the mean of a variable for the two groups. If the difference is big enough compared with the estimated standard error, there is evidence that the population means differ.

## Activity 6　*Does the type of school matter?*

In the state sector, secondary schools are not all managed in the same way. One type of school is a 'community school'. So, a question that can be posed is:

> *On average, is the GCSE headline figure ($P_{KS4}$) the same in community schools as in other schools?*

For schools in our sample, the following summary statistics were obtained.

**Table 2**　Summary statistics for $P_{KS4}$ by type of school

|  | Sample size | Sample mean (%) | Sample standard deviation (%) |
|---|---|---|---|
| Community school | 43 | 49.8 | 13.55 |
| Other school | 57 | 50.7 | 19.61 |

The procedure for carrying out a two-sample $z$-test was detailed in Section 6 of Unit 7.

Carry out a two-sided two-sample $z$-test to investigate whether the population mean of $P_{KS4}$ in community schools and the population mean of $P_{KS4}$ in other schools are equal.

However, as you may already have realised, not all potential factors neatly split schools into two groups. For example, one possible factor that might influence a school's GCSE headline figure is the academic ability of students before they join the school. This can be measured, if imperfectly, by considering the performance in national tests of students when they ended Key Stage 2.

### National Curriculum tests – SATs

Towards the end of Key Stage 2, children in English schools take National Curriculum tests, often referred to as 'SATs', in English, Mathematics and Science. In each test, a child is recorded as being at Level 5, Level 4, Level 3, Level 2 or below Level 2. These levels are then converted into points using the following scale.

Level 5: 33 points, Level 4: 27 points, Level 3: 21 points, Level 2 or below: 15 points.

(Source: Department for Education (2011) 'Test and examination point scores used in the 2011 school and college performance tables')

So one measure of the ability of students when they join a secondary school is as follows.

$P_{KS2}$ – the average points score (APS) at the end of Key Stage 2

For the 100 schools in our sample, the value of $P_{KS2}$ for the students just finishing Key Stage 4 in 2011 ranges from 24.2 to 30.5. A histogram of $P_{KS2}$ (Figure 2) shows that the values do not fall neatly into two groups. So, the two-sample $z$-test cannot be used to investigate whether $P_{KS2}$ influences $P_{KS4}$. A different approach is needed.

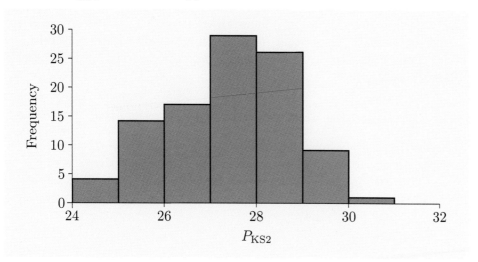

**Figure 2**   Histogram of $P_{KS2}$ at intake for students at the end of Key Stage 4 in 100 schools

The variables $P_{KS4}$ and $P_{KS2}$ are an example of linked data. A value of $P_{KS4}$ and $P_{KS2}$ is available for each school in our sample. In Unit 5 you explored relationships in linked data by fitting lines. These lines summarise the relationship between two variables. However, the lines do not provide information about how strong the relationship is – that is, how accurately one variable can be predicted from knowledge about the value of the other variable. In the next section a measure of the strength of relationships is introduced – the correlation coefficient.

Linked data were introduced in Subsection 1.2 of Unit 5.

## Exercises on Section 1

**Exercise 1**   *Use a two-sample* z*-test?*

Below, four possible factors that might affect the quality of a secondary school are listed (where the quality of a secondary school is assumed to be measured using $P_{KS4}$). Which of the following factors could be tested using a $z$-test?

1.   Whether the school has a sixth form.

2.   The size of the school (as measured by the number of students finishing Key Stage 4).

3.   Whether the school allows students to take some GCSEs a year early.

4.   The proportion of students eligible for free school meals.

# 2  The correlation coefficient

As briefly mentioned at the end of Section 1, the correlation coefficient is a measure of the strength of a relationship between two linked variables. Before going on to find out how the correlation coefficient is calculated by hand in Subsection 2.2, we first focus on what range of values a correlation coefficient can take. (Note that in Subsection 2.4 you will be referred to the Computer Book to learn how to calculate the correlation coefficient using Minitab.)

## 2.1  Introducing the correlation coefficient

In Subsection 2.3 of Unit 5, the concept of the strength of relationships was introduced. In that unit, strength was judged subjectively from a scatterplot. Strong relationships are those where the points lie close to a line. Conversely, weak relationships are those where the points on the scatterplot only loosely follow a line.

**Activity 7**   *Strong or weak?*

For each of the scatterplots shown below, discuss whether the relationship between the two variables is strong or weak.

**Figure 3**

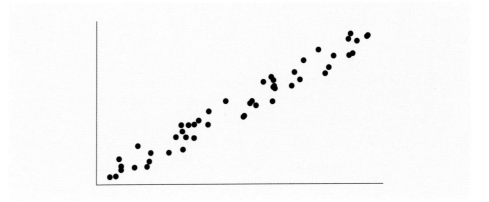

**Figure 4**

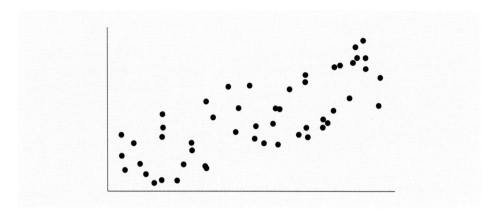

**Figure 5**

It is difficult to say how strong a relationship is just by looking at a
scatterplot. The scatterplot only gives us a subjective impression of the
strength of a relationship. What is needed is a single numerical quantity to
summarise the strength of relationship between two variables – a
*correlation coefficient.*

### Correlation coefficient

A **correlation coefficient** is a number which summarises the
strength of relationship between two variables.

A correlation coefficient always takes a value between −1 and +1. When
there is an exact positive linear relationship between two variables, the
value of the correlation coefficient is equal to +1, its maximum value.
When there is an exact negative linear relationship between two variables,
the value of the correlation coefficient is −1, its minimum value.

More than one correlation coefficient has been invented by statisticians –
each measuring the strength of a relationship in a particular way. The
coefficient we use in this module is sometimes called the 'Pearson
product–moment correlation coefficient', to distinguish it from the other
correlation coefficients.

**Example 1**   *Relationships with a correlation coefficient of* $+1$

In Figure 6 two scatterplots are shown. In each scatterplot the correlation coefficient is $+1$ because both depict an exact positive linear relationship. Note that the slope of the relationship is not important.

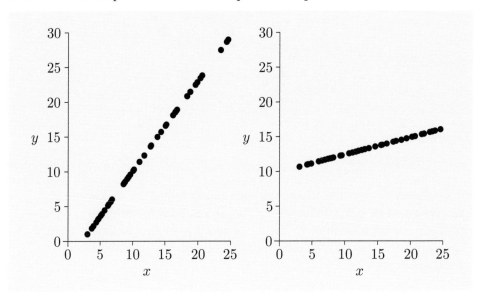

**Figure 6**   Scatterplots of two sets of artificial data

**Example 2**   *Relationships with a correlation coefficient of* $-1$

Two examples of relationships which have a correlation coefficient of $-1$ are shown in Figure 7. Notice that in both cases the points all lie exactly in a line and that the slope of the line is negative (that is, the line goes down from left to right).

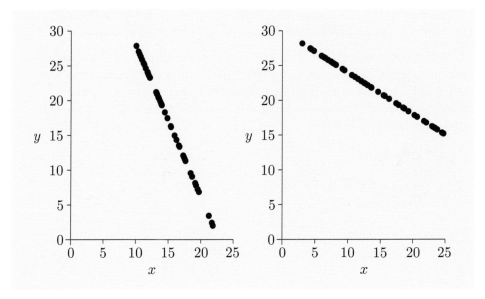

**Figure 7**   Scatterplots of two more sets of artificial data

For any relationship that is not exactly linear, the correlation coefficient lies somewhere between $+1$ and $-1$. A positive relationship has a positive correlation coefficient, and a negative relationship has a negative coefficient. If there is no relationship between the two variables, then the correlation coefficient is equal to, or very close to, zero.

In Figure 8 and for the remainder of this module, the symbol $r$ is used for the correlation coefficient. If you look at Figure 8 now, you will start to get a feeling for what is implied by various values of $r$. In (a), the points all lie quite close to an imaginary straight line sloping upwards (from left to right), and the correlation coefficient is $+0.9$. If we drew an area to include all the points, it would be long and thin. In (b) there is also a positive relationship between the two variables, but it is much less pronounced and the coefficient is only $+0.5$. An area including these points would be much fatter than that for (a). In (c), we cannot really see any relationship between the two variables; if we drew an area to include these points, it would more or less cover the whole plot. This is confirmed by the small value of $r$, which is $+0.1$. The plots in (d), (e) and (f) all show negative correlations.

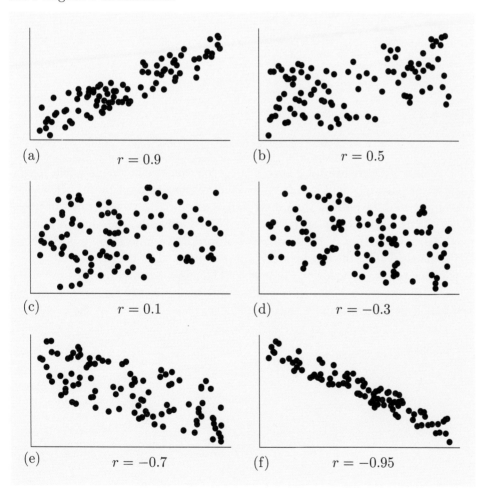

(a)  $r = 0.9$

(b)  $r = 0.5$

(c)  $r = 0.1$

(d)  $r = -0.3$

(e)  $r = -0.7$

(f)  $r = -0.95$

**Figure 8**

**Activity 8**   *Estimating correlations*

Look at Figure 9 and guess the correlation coefficient in each of the cases shown in (a), (b) and (c). You need not be surprised if you do not get very close to the true values, but you should at least get the sign right and probably be within about 0.2 or 0.3.

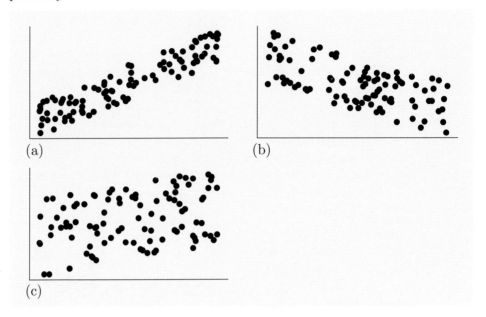

(a)

(b)

(c)

**Figure 9**

In the special case that the two data points are exactly horizontally or vertically aligned, $r$ is undefined.

One point worth mentioning is that a correlation coefficient is much more meaningful if it is calculated from a large number of data points. If there are only two data points, then a straight line can always be drawn between them. Thus $r$ will equal $+1$ (if the line slopes upwards) or $-1$ (if it slopes downwards). Neither of these values is appropriate unless there is a precise mathematical relationship between the variables. The correlation coefficient takes the value 0.5 in each of the cases (a), (b) and (c) in Figure 10, but the relationship is most convincing in the scatterplot in (c) because it is based on more data.

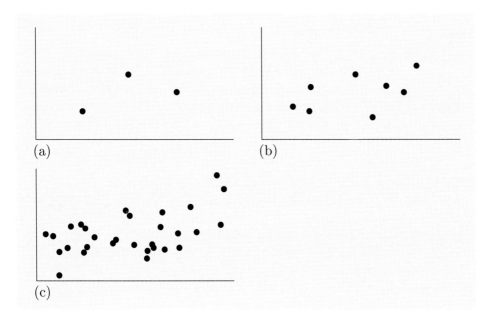

**Figure 10**

*You have now covered the material related to Screencast 1 for Unit 9 (see the M140 website).*

## 2.2  Calculating the correlation coefficient by hand

In this subsection the calculation of the correlation coefficient by hand will be demonstrated. This is done in Examples 3 to 5, where the correlation coefficient is calculated for the relationship between (i) the performance of groups of students at Key Stage 2 and (ii) the subsequent performance of broadly the same groups of students at Key Stage 4.

The following is the formula for the correlation coefficient:

$$\text{Correlation} = \frac{\sum(x - \bar{x})(y - \bar{y})}{\sqrt{\sum(x - \bar{x})^2 \times \sum(y - \bar{y})^2}}$$

If you compare this formula with that for the slope of the least squares regression line (see Subsection 4.2 of Unit 5), you will notice that some of the elements that make up the formulas are the same. This similarity means that the calculation of the correlation coefficient has a lot in common with the calculation of the least squares regression line.

Like the calculation of the slope of the least squares regression line, the first step includes calculating the sum of all the $x$-values ($\sum x$), the sum of all the $y$-values ($\sum y$), the sum of the squares of all the $x$-values ($\sum x^2$), and the sum of the products of the $x$- and $y$-values ($\sum xy$). It also includes the calculation of an extra sum, the sum of the squares of all the $y$-values ($\sum y^2$). In summary, step 1 is the calculation of

$$\sum x, \quad \sum y, \quad \sum x^2, \quad \sum y^2 \quad \text{and} \quad \sum xy.$$

**Example 3**    *Calculating a correlation coefficient – step 1*

The data we will use relate to students in Wales. In 2011, school-level data for Welsh schools were not made publicly available. Instead the data were just grouped by Welsh Assembly constituency. For the purpose of this calculation we look at eight of these constituencies, taking performances at Key Stage 4 in 2011 as the $y$-values. Students who ended Key Stage 4 in 2011 would have ended Key Stage 2 in 2006 – the constituencies' performances at Key Stage 2 in 2006 will be the $x$-values.

More specifically, the measure of performance at Key Stage 4 ($y$) will be the percentage of students achieving the following benchmark (similar to the GCSE headline figure, $P_{KS4}$) – the equivalent of five grade A* to C GCSEs including GCSE Mathematics and GCSE English or GCSE Welsh first language. The measure at Key Stage 2 ($x$) will be the percentage of students who attained the following benchmark – at least Level 4 in specified subjects. We will calculate the correlation coefficient for the relationship between these two measures.

The data are as follows:

| $x$ | 78.9 | 75.8 | 77.3 | 74.2 | 78.1 | 72.8 | 77.6 | 77.9 |
|-----|------|------|------|------|------|------|------|------|
| $y$ | 56.7 | 53.1 | 56.1 | 55.9 | 54.1 | 48.6 | 59.4 | 54.0 |

The sums of all the $x$-values and of all the $y$-values are as follows:

$$\sum x = 78.9 + 75.8 + \cdots + 77.9 = 612.6,$$

$$\sum y = 56.7 + 53.1 + \cdots + 54.0 = 437.9.$$

We also require the sum of squares of the $x$-values, the sum of squares of the $y$-values and the sum of products of the $x$- and $y$-values. You should be able to find these three sums on your calculator without writing down each square (or product) separately.

$$\sum x^2 = 78.9^2 + 75.8^2 + \cdots + 77.9^2$$
$$= 46\,941.4,$$

$$\sum y^2 = 56.7^2 + 53.1^2 + \cdots + 54.0^2$$
$$= 24\,039.65,$$

$$\sum xy = 78.9 \times 56.7 + 75.8 \times 53.1 + \cdots + 77.9 \times 54.0$$
$$= 33\,562.25.$$

These five sums are the basic quantities you need, and this completes the first step of the calculation.

---

The next step is to calculate the sum of squared deviations of the $x$-values and also the sum of products of the deviations of the $x$- and $y$-values. You have previously calculated these quantities when calculating a regression line. In addition, the sum of squared deviations of the $y$-values must also be calculated.

That is, the second step is to calculate

$$\sum(x-\overline{x})^2, \quad \sum(y-\overline{y})^2 \quad \text{and} \quad \sum(x-\overline{x})(y-\overline{y}).$$

---

**Example 4**   *Calculating a correlation coefficient – step 2*

There are eight observations, so $n = 8$.

$$\sum(x-\overline{x})^2 = \sum x^2 - \frac{(\sum x)^2}{n}$$

$$= 46\,941.4 - \frac{612.6^2}{8}$$

$$= 46\,941.4 - 46\,909.845 = 31.555.$$

The values calculated above are not rounded as they are going to be used in the next step of the calculation.

$$\sum(y-\overline{y})^2 = \sum y^2 - \frac{(\sum y)^2}{n}$$

$$= 24\,039.65 - \frac{437.9^2}{8}$$

$$= 24\,039.65 - 23\,969.551\,25 = 70.098\,75.$$

$$\sum(x-\overline{x})(y-\overline{y}) = \sum xy - \frac{(\sum x)(\sum y)}{n}$$

$$= 33\,562.25 - \frac{612.6 \times 437.9}{8}$$

$$= 33\,562.25 - 33\,532.1925 = 30.0575.$$

---

Step 3 uses the results of step 2 to obtain the correlation coefficient.

---

**Example 5**   *Calculating a correlation coefficient – step 3*

The formula for the correlation coefficient is

$$\text{correlation} = \frac{\sum(x-\overline{x})(y-\overline{y})}{\sqrt{\sum(x-\overline{x})^2 \times \sum(y-\overline{y})^2}},$$

so in this example,

$$\text{correlation} = \frac{30.0575}{\sqrt{31.555 \times 70.098\,75}}$$

$$\simeq \frac{30.0575}{47.0315} \simeq 0.639\,09.$$

The correlation coefficient is therefore 0.64 (to two decimal places).

---

The procedure for calculating the correlation coefficient is summarised below.

Calculating the correlation coefficient

Given a batch of $n$ linked data pairs, $(x, y)$, the correlation coefficient $(r)$ is obtained as follows:

1.  Calculate $\sum x$, $\sum y$, $\sum x^2$, $\sum y^2$ and $\sum xy$.

2.  Calculate

$$\sum (x - \bar{x})^2 = \sum x^2 - \frac{1}{n} \left( \sum x \right)^2 ,$$

$$\sum (y - \bar{y})^2 = \sum y^2 - \frac{1}{n} \left( \sum y \right)^2 ,$$

$$\sum (x - \bar{x})(y - \bar{y}) = \sum xy - \frac{1}{n} \left( \sum x \right) \left( \sum y \right) .$$

3.  Use the values from step 2 to calculate

$$r = \frac{\sum (x - \bar{x})(y - \bar{y})}{\sqrt{\sum (x - \bar{x})^2 \times \sum (y - \bar{y})^2}} .$$

The next activities provide practice in calculating a correlation coefficient.

**Activity 9**　*Calculating a correlation coefficient*

In Examples 3 to 5 a correlation coefficient was calculated for data on student performance in constituencies of one Welsh region, Mid and West Wales. Data for constituencies in other Welsh regions are also available. In particular, data relating to seven constituencies in South Wales West are given in Table 3 below.

**Table 3**　Results for Key Stage 2 in 2006 and Key Stage 4 in 2011

| Percentage achieving benchmark at Key Stage 2 in 2006 | Percentage achieving benchmark at Key Stage 4 in 2011 |
| --- | --- |
| 67.2 | 45.1 |
| 76.0 | 48.3 |
| 80.6 | 65.5 |
| 72.3 | 56.4 |
| 71.0 | 41.9 |
| 66.9 | 40.1 |
| 74.0 | 58.3 |

(a)  Calculate the correlation coefficient between attainment at Key Stage 2 and attainment at Key Stage 4, based on these data.

(b) A scatterplot of the data is given in Figure 11. In the light of this scatterplot, does your answer to part (a) make sense?

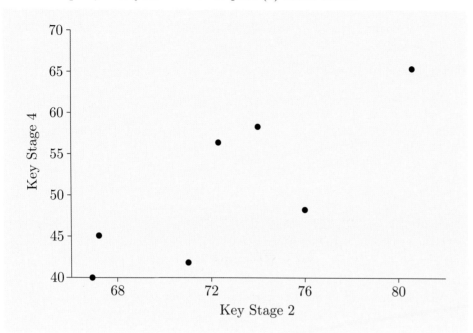

**Figure 11**   Percentage of children in the assembly constituencies of South Wales West achieving particular benchmarks at Key Stage 2 in 2006 and Key Stage 4 in 2011

'Correlation Street'

**Activity 10**   *Barbecue weather?*

Table 4 gives the temperature $(x\,^{\circ}\text{C})$ on the day before a public holiday in May for the last eight years and the number of barbecue sets a store sold that day $(y)$.

**Table 4**   Temperature $(x\,^{\circ}\text{C})$ and sales of barbecue sets $(y)$

| $x$ | 16 | 13 | 21 | 17 | 15 | 20 | 15 | 18 |
|---|---|---|---|---|---|---|---|---|
| $y$ | 4 | 2 | 7 | 4 | 5 | 8 | 4 | 6 |

For these data:

$$\sum x = 135, \quad \sum y = 40,$$
$$\sum x^2 = 2329, \quad \sum y^2 = 226, \quad \sum xy = 708.$$

Calculate the correlation coefficient between temperature and number of barbecue sets sold, based on these data.

*You have now covered the material related to Screencast 2 for Unit 9 (see the M140 website).*

## 2.3   The sign of the correlation coefficient

We have said that the correlation coefficient is positive when there is a positive linear relationship between $x$ and $y$, and negative when there is a negative linear relationship between them. To consider why, suppose we have a sample of linked $x$- and $y$-values. In some $(x, y)$ pairs, both $x$ and $y$ will be greater than average, sometimes both will be smaller than average, and sometimes one will be larger and the other will be smaller. If $x$ and $y$ are both greater than average, then $(x - \overline{x})$ and $(y - \overline{y})$ are both positive, so

$$(x - \overline{x})(y - \overline{y})$$

is positive. Then that $(x, y)$ pair will contribute a positive amount to the numerator of

$$r = \frac{\sum(x - \overline{x})(y - \overline{y})}{\sqrt{\sum(x - \overline{x})^2 \times \sum(y - \overline{y})^2}}.$$

On the other hand, if $x$ is greater than average while $y$ is smaller than average, then $(x - \overline{x})$ is positive while $(y - \overline{y})$ is negative, so

$$(x - \overline{x})(y - \overline{y})$$

is negative. Hence, that $(x, y)$ pair will contribute a negative amount to the numerator of $r$. Table 5 shows which $(x, y)$ pairs contribute a positive amount to the numerator of $r$, and which contribute a negative amount.

**Table 5**   The sign of contributions to the correlation coefficient

| $x$-value | $y$-value | $x - \overline{x}$ | $y - \overline{y}$ | $(x - \overline{x})(y - \overline{y})$ |
|---|---|---|---|---|
| greater than $\overline{x}$ | greater than $\overline{y}$ | positive | positive | positive |
| less than $\overline{x}$ | less than $\overline{y}$ | negative | negative | positive |
| greater than $\overline{x}$ | less than $\overline{y}$ | positive | negative | negative |
| less than $\overline{x}$ | greater than $\overline{y}$ | negative | positive | negative |

Pictorially, Table 5 corresponds to the following areas on the scatterplot in Figure 12.

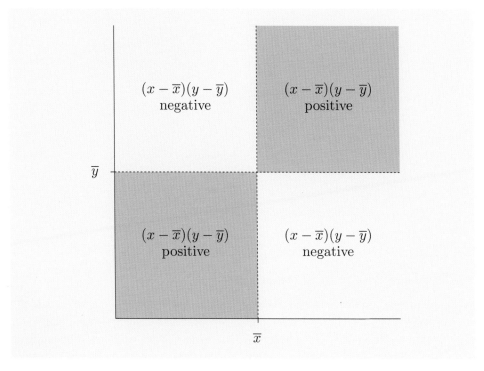

**Figure 12**   Contributions to the numerator of the correlation coefficient

Now if most data points are in the shaded areas (top right and bottom left), then

- most points will contribute a positive amount to the numerator of $r$
- the regression line through the data will slope upwards, and there is a positive linear relationship between $x$ and $y$.

On the other hand, if most data points are in the non-shaded areas (top left and bottom right), then

- most points will contribute a negative amount to the numerator of $r$
- the regression line through the data will slope downwards, and there is a negative linear relationship between $x$ and $y$.

Finally, note that because the denominator of the formula for $r$ is always positive, the sign of the correlation is always the same as the sign of the numerator. Hence, the correlation coefficient is positive when there is a positive linear relationship and negative when there is a negative linear relationship.

**Example 6**   *Deducing the sign of the correlation coefficient*

In Figure 13 a dataset consisting of 20 observations is plotted. Also, the regions where $(x - \overline{x})(y - \overline{y})$ is positive are shaded.

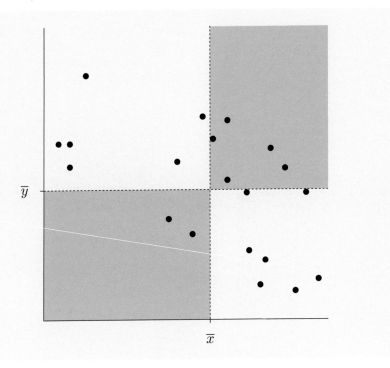

**Figure 13**   A dataset of 20 observations

Notice that, in this plot, just seven of the twenty points lie in the shaded region. These will give a positive contribution to the numerator of the correlation coefficients. However, they are outweighed by the points giving a negative contribution to the numerator, as there are thirteen such points. (Also, points $(x, y)$ make a greater contribution to $\sum (x - \overline{x})(y - \overline{y})$ as they get further from $(\overline{x}, \overline{y})$, and the points in the non-shaded regions tend to be further from $(\overline{x}, \overline{y})$ than the points in the shaded regions.)

So overall the correlation coefficient will be negative (as it should be for variables that are clearly negatively related). In fact the correlation coefficient turns out to be $r = -0.57$.

**Activity 11**  *Deducing the sign of another correlation coefficient*

A different dataset of 20 observations is plotted in Figure 14. The regions where $(x - \overline{x})(y - \overline{y})$ is positive are shaded.

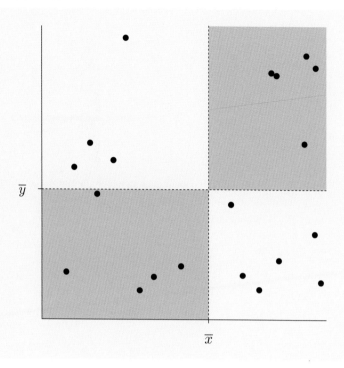

**Figure 14**  Another dataset of 20 observations

(a) On the basis of this plot, does there appear to be a positive relationship, a negative relationship or no relationship?

(b) By considering contributions to the numerator of the correlation coefficient, is the correlation coefficient likely to be positive, negative or close to zero?

## 2.4 Computer work: correlation coefficients

As you have seen in Subsection 2.2, calculating the correlation coefficient by hand is straightforward. However, the calculations are tedious, particularly when the dataset is not small. So it is far more common to use a computer instead.

In this subsection you will learn how to calculate a correlation coefficient using Minitab. You should now turn to Chapter 9 of the Computer Book and work through Subsection 9.1.

## Exercises on Section 2

**Exercise 2**    *Ordering correlations*

Order the following correlations from strongest to weakest.

$$+0.25 \quad +0.80 \quad -0.30 \quad -0.99 \quad +0.04$$

**Exercise 3**    *Estimating more correlations*

Figure 15 shows a scatterplot of the best times for the 200-metre sprint and 100-metre sprint by male UK sprinters in 2011.

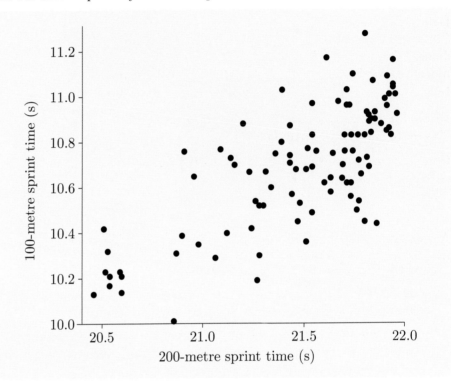

**Figure 15**    Times for male UK sprinters in 2011

(Source: TOPS in Athletics, December 2011)

Using this plot, estimate the correlation between the best time on the 200-metre sprint and the best time on the 100-metre sprint.

**Exercise 4**  *Calculating another correlation coefficient*

The data for the top nine sprinters in the 200-metre sprint plotted in
Figure 15 are given in Table 6 below.

**Table 6**   Best performances of top nine sprinters

| Name | 200-metre time (s) | 100-metre time (s) |
|------|--------------------|--------------------|
| Harry Aikines-Aryeety | 20.46 | 10.13 |
| Leon Baptiste | 20.51 | 10.42 |
| James Ellington | 20.52 | 10.23 |
| Richard Kilty | 20.53 | 10.32 |
| Danny Talbot | 20.54 | 10.21 |
| Christian Malcolm | 20.54 | 10.17 |
| James Alaka | 20.59 | 10.23 |
| Marlon Devonish | 20.60 | 10.14 |
| Luke Fagan | 20.60 | 10.21 |

Using these data, calculate by hand the correlation coefficient between the
200-metre time and the 100-metre time for this group of sprinters.

Compare the correlation coefficient for these nine sprinters with the
correlation coefficient in Exercise 3.

Marlon Devonish in action

**Exercise 5**  *Deducing the sign of yet another correlation coefficient*

A dataset of 20 observations is plotted in Figure 16. The regions where
$(x - \overline{x})(y - \overline{y})$ is positive are shaded.

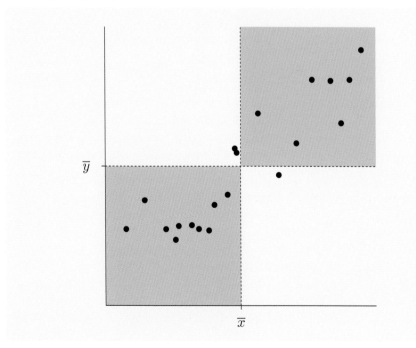

**Figure 16**   A dataset of 20 observations

(a) On the basis of this plot, does there appear to be a positive
relationship, a negative relationship or no relationship?

(b) By considering contributions to the numerator of the correlation coefficient, is the correlation coefficient likely to be positive, negative or close to zero?

# 3   More on the correlation coefficient

In Section 2 you saw that the correlation coefficient is a measure of the strength of a relationship. There you saw that the correlation coefficient takes a value between $+1$ and $-1$, with $+1$ indicating an exact positive relationship, $-1$ indicating an exact negative relationship, and 0 indicating no relationship. In this section we shall look further at what aspects of the data affect the value of the correlation coefficient.

## 3.1   Specifying the variables

In Figures 8 to 10 in Subsection 2.1, which consisted of made-up data, you may have noticed that no scales were included. In general, this is very bad practice for a graph, but in this case there was a specific reason.

> The correlation coefficient does not depend on the scales of the axes. It only reflects the pattern of the points.

Let us see what this means by looking at the following example.

**Example 7**   *Pass rates in English and Mathematics*

Figure 17 shows data on pass rates in English and Mathematics qualifications at Key Stage 4 for the 100 English secondary schools in our sample. You can see that there is a definite positive correlation between the pass rates in English and Mathematics in the schools; the correlation coefficient turns out to be $+0.70$.

Now, suppose that instead of plotting the pass rates in English as given, we plot them as rates (percentages) over 50%. So a pass rate of 80% in English will appear as $+30$ and a pass rate of 40% will appear as $-10$. Also, we could plot the pass rates in Mathematics as proportions more than 0.5. So a pass rate of 80% in Mathematics will appear as $+0.3$ and a pass rate of 40% will appear as $-0.1$. Then the scatterplot appears as in Figure 18 and though the numbers on the axes are different, the pattern of points is exactly the same as in Figure 17. The correlation coefficient does not change; it is still $r = +0.70$.

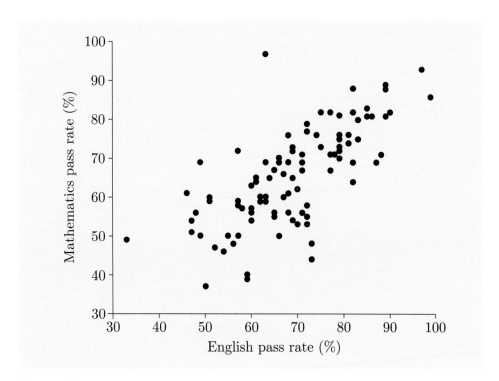

**Figure 17**   Pass rates in English and Mathematics at Key Stage 4 for 100 non-selective schools

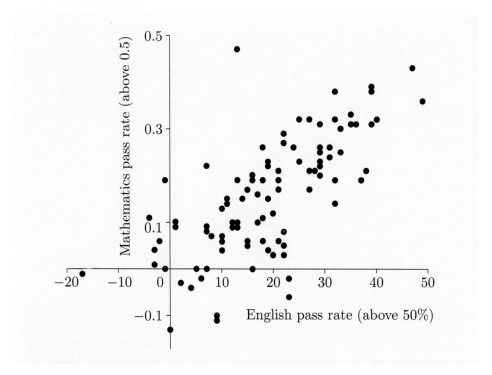

**Figure 18**   Pass rates in English and Mathematics at Key Stage 4 for 100 non-selective schools

So the coefficient is not changed either by changing the position of one or both axes or by recording measurements in different units.

In Figures 17 and 18, the pattern of points looks exactly the same, although the numbers are different. However, it also does not make any difference if one of the scales is changed so that the pattern looks different. This has been done in Figure 19. The correlation coefficient is still $+0.70$ in this scatterplot. It is the amount of scatter about a straight line that is important, not how steep the line is. In all these figures, the points could all be included inside a fairly narrow region.

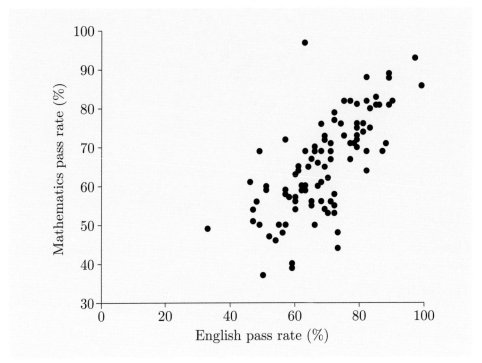

**Figure 19**   Pass rates in English and Mathematics at Key Stage 4 for 100 non-selective schools

Another factor which does not affect the value of the correlation coefficient is which variable is plotted on the $x$-axis. In this example, there is no obvious reason why either one of the variables is dependent on the other, and in Figure 20, the pass rates for Mathematics are plotted on the $x$-axis, and the pass rates for English on the $y$-axis. Although the pattern of points in the scatterplot looks different, the value of the correlation coefficient is still unchanged at $+0.70$.

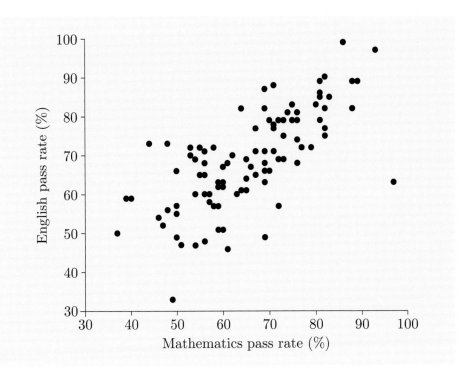

**Figure 20** Pass rates in English and Mathematics at Key Stage 4 for 100 non-selective schools

Thus we have the following.

> The correlation coefficient does not depend on which variable is plotted on the vertical axis and which is plotted on the horizontal axis.

## Activity 12    *Same correlation?*

Suppose that the correlation is $+0.56$ for the following pair of variables: a car's weight (in tonnes) and the miles per gallon it can achieve. Which of the following pairs of variables would have exactly the same correlation as this pair?

1.  A car's weight (in kilograms) and the miles per gallon it can achieve.

2.  A car's length (in metres) and the miles per gallon it can achieve.

3.  A car's weight (in tonnes) and the kilometres per litre it can achieve.

4.  A car's weight (in tonnes) and its fuel consumption (measured in litres per kilometre).

5.  The miles per gallon over 50 miles per gallon that a car can achieve, and a car's weight (in tonnes over 1 tonne).

## 3.2  The shape of the relationship

In Subsection 2.1 you learned that if there is no relationship between two variables, the correlation coefficient is equal to, or very close to, zero. Does that mean that when the correlation coefficient between variables is close to zero, there is no relationship between the variables? The answer is: *not necessarily.*

---

**Example 8**  *A curve with zero correlation*

Figure 21 is a scatterplot of some made-up data. For these data it also turns out that $r = 0.0$.

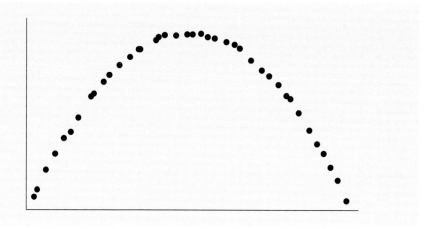

**Figure 21**  A scatterplot of some data

However, notice that despite this zero correlation, there is clearly a very strong relationship between the two variables.

---

So why does the strong relationship between the two variables plotted in Example 8 have a correlation coefficient of zero? The answer is that the correlation coefficient $r$ only measures the extent of the *linear* relationship between two variables. It does not take account of a non-linear pattern in the relationship.

> A correlation coefficient close to zero does *not* imply that there is no relationship, merely that there is not a linear relationship.

However, not all non-linear relationships will have a correlation coefficient close to zero, as the next example shows.

**Example 9**   *Key Stage 2 pass rates*

In Figure 22, the percentage of pupils in England passing their Key Stage 2 test in English at Level 4 or above between 1995 and 2011 is plotted. Notice from the plot that there seems to be a close positive relationship between percentage pass rate and year: a smooth curve could be drawn on the graph that is very close to all the points. However, the relationship is not linear. In the late 1990s, the pass rate went up rapidly. In contrast, the pass rate only went up by a few percentage points in the period 2004 to 2011.

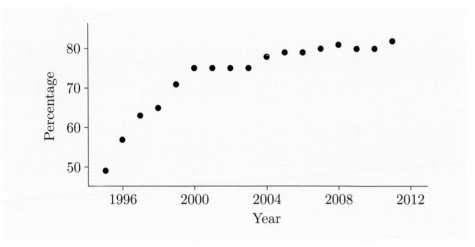

**Figure 22**   Percentage of Key Stage 2 students at Level 4 or above in English over time

For these data, $r = +0.88$. This is quite close to $+1$. However, such a close relationship between two quantities would give a much bigger value of $r$ – between $+0.95$ and $+0.99$ – if the relationship were linear.

The correlation coefficient just measures the strength of a linear relationship. When a non-linear relationship is generally positive, the correlation coefficient will be positive but not as large as for a similarly strong positive *linear* relationship. Equally, when a non-linear relationship is generally negative, the correlation coefficient will be negative, but not as negative as for a similarly strong negative linear relationship.

**Activity 13**   *Representative correlation?*

For each of the scatterplots shown below, state whether the correlation coefficient is likely to be a good indication of the strength of the relationship between the two variables.

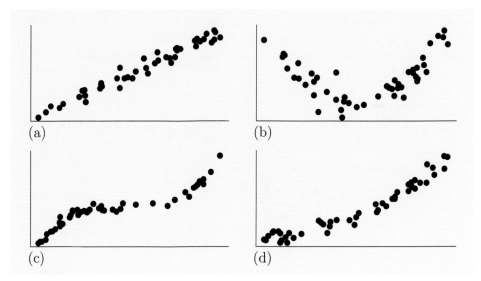

**Figure 23**

## 3.3   Outliers and influential points

The purpose of this subsection is to show how one or two data points can sometimes have an overriding effect on a correlation coefficient. It can happen in two possible ways. First, look at Figure 24, which gives a scatterplot of the number of boys and the number of girls reaching the end of Key Stage 4 in our sample of 100 schools.

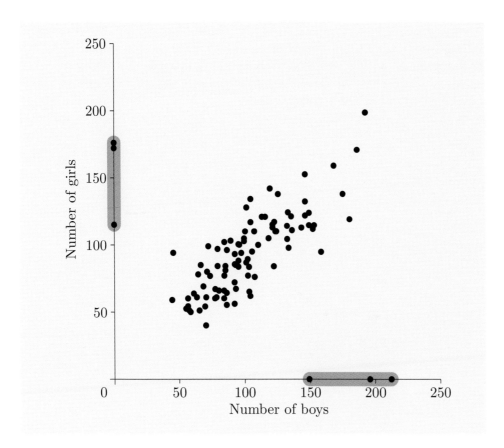

**Figure 24**   Numbers of boys and girls ending Key Stage 4

In this scatterplot two groups of points have been highlighted: a group of three schools where there were no girls and a group of three schools where there were no boys. These schools do not follow the pattern of the other schools, which tended to have similar numbers of boys and girls. These points are therefore outliers. In fact, these six schools are single-sex schools, whereas all the other schools are mixed-sex schools. The point to notice here is that when the seven single sex schools are included, the correlation coefficient is +0.23; when they are omitted, the coefficient is +0.74. So, if only mixed-sex schools are included, the relationship between the numbers of boys and girls in schools ending Key Stage 4 is strong and positive; but if all schools are included, the relationship is weak.

The second way in which a very small number of points can exert an overriding effect is shown in Figure 25. The $x$-variable is the percentage of children who achieved the Key Stage 2 benchmark in 2006 and the $y$-variable is the percentage of children who achieved the Key Stage 4 benchmark in 2011, both introduced in Example 3 (Subsection 2.2).

The ringed point refers to one particular constituency, Llanelli. You can see that the ringed point is **remote** from the rest; the percentage of children achieving the Key Stage 2 benchmark and the percentage achieving the Key Stage 4 benchmark were both noticeably lower in Llanelli than in the other constituencies.

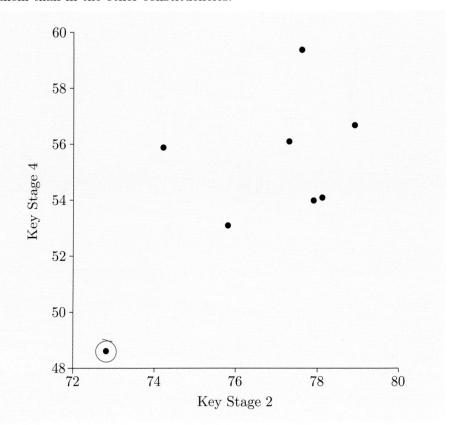

**Figure 25**   Percentage of children achieving particular benchmarks at Key Stage 2 in 2006 and Key Stage 4 in 2011

The point cannot be considered an outlier because it does not appear to be out of line with the remaining points. However, without that point, the correlation would be much less pronounced; the coefficient is reduced from +0.64 to +0.18 if the point for Llanelli is omitted. Such a point is sometimes called an **influential point**. An influential point has an $x$-value and/or a $y$-value that is a long way from those of the other points.

It is worth noting that removing an influential point *reduces* the amount of correlation (i.e. moves the correlation coefficient closer to zero), whereas removing an outlier usually *increases* it (moves the coefficient towards +1 or −1).

**Activity 14**   *Spotting outliers and influential points*

Data are also available for other regions of Wales, and data for the eight constituencies in South Wales East are plotted in Figure 26.

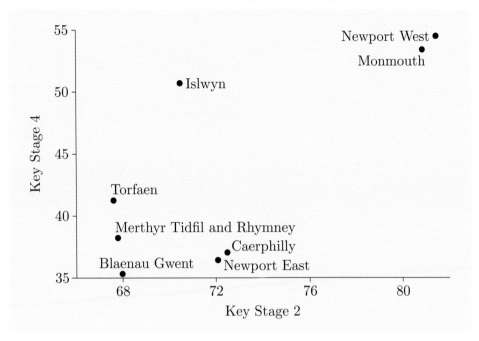

**Figure 26**   Percentage of children in the assembly constituencies of South Wales East achieving particular benchmarks at Key Stage 2 in 2006 and Key Stage 4 in 2011

Identify any points which are outliers or influential points, and make rough guesses of the correlation coefficients both including and excluding these points.

*You have now covered the material related to Screencast 3 for Unit 9 (see the M140 website).*

## 3.4   Correlation and causation

The final point we shall note about correlations is the following.

Correlation is *not* causation.

That is, just because two variables are correlated does not mean that one causes the other.

**Example 10**   *Pass rates in English and Mathematics*

In Example 7 (Subsection 3.1) you saw that there is a strong positive correlation between a school's pass rate in English and its pass rate in Mathematics. However, does this mean that a high rate pass rate in Mathematics causes a high pass rate in English?

That is, can the relationship be summarised by the diagram in Figure 27? (In such diagrams the arrow denotes a **causal relationship**.)

**Figure 27**   A possible relationship between pass rates in English and Mathematics

No, it does not. It could be the other way round – a high pass rate in English might cause a high pass rate in Mathematics, as shown in Figure 28. The correlation would be the same.

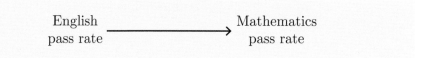

**Figure 28**   Another possible relationship between pass rates in English and Mathematics

However, it is more likely that the actual causal relationships are closer to one of those shown in Figures 29 and 30. That is, the relationship between the pass rates in English and Mathematics are due to some other causal relationship, such as the ability of students and/or the quality of the school.

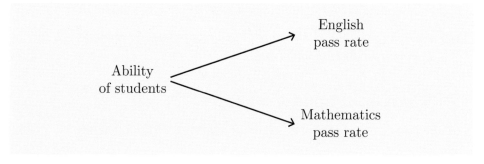

**Figure 29**   Another possible relationship between pass rates in English and Mathematics

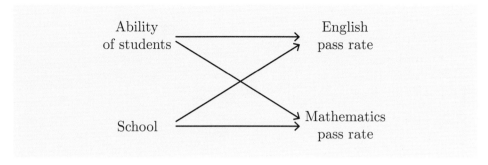

**Figure 30**   Yet another possible relationship between pass rates in English and Mathematics

From just the correlation coefficient, it is impossible to tell which of these situations represents the true causal relationships – if any of them do! They can all lead to a high positive correlation between the English and Mathematics pass rates.

## Activity 15    *Does chocolate make you clever?*

In November 2012, the BBC News website reported on a study about a country's chocolate consumption and the country's number of Nobel prize laureates. A plot from that report is reproduced in Figure 31.

The correlation coefficient is shown on Figure 31; its value is $+0.791$. Does this correlation coefficient provide evidence that high chocolate consumption makes a country's inhabitants clever?

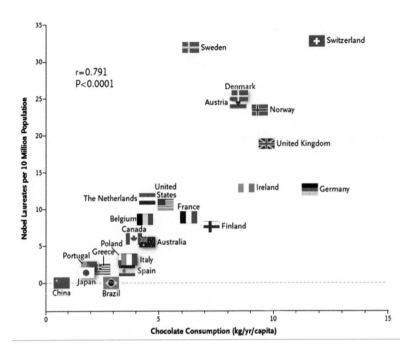

**Figure 31**   Chocolate consumption and numbers of Nobel prize laureates

(Source: BBC News website (19 November 2012) reporting on Messerli, F. (2012) 'Chocolate consumption, cognitive function and Nobel laureates', *New England Journal of Medicine*, vol. 367, pp. 1562–1564)

## Exercises on Section 3

### Exercise 6   *Does the correlation coefficient change?*

In Activity 10 (Subsection 2.2) you calculated the correlation coefficient between the temperature ($x$) on the day before a public holiday and the number of barbecue sets a store sold that day ($y$). This correlation coefficient turned out to be $+0.91$.

(a) If the number of barbecue sets that were sold had been recorded as $x$ and temperature had been recorded as $y$, would the correlation coefficient be different?

(b) The temperature was recorded in *degrees Celsius* (°C). Another temperature scale is the *Kelvin scale* (K). A temperature measured in degrees Celsius can be converted to kelvins simply by adding 273.15. For example, a temperature of 16 °C is 289.15 K. If temperatures had been measured on the Kelvin scale, rather than in degrees Celsius, would the correlation coefficient be different?

(c) Another scale that is used to record temperature is the *Fahrenheit scale* (°F). To convert a temperature from Celsius to Fahrenheit, you first multiply the temperature by 1.8, and then you add 32 to the result. For 16 °C the calculation is as follows: $(16 \times 1.8) + 32 = 60.8$. So 16 °C is the same as 60.8 °F. If temperatures had been measured in degrees Fahrenheit, rather than in degrees Celsius, would the correlation coefficient be different?

---

**Exercise 7**   *Estimating yet more correlations*

In Exercise 4 (Section 2) you were asked to calculate the correlation coefficient between the best time for the 200-metre sprint and the best time for the 100-metre sprint, based on nine UK sprinters. A plot of these times is given in Figure 32.

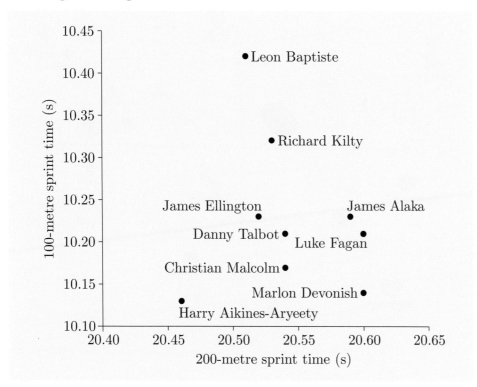

**Figure 32**   Times for top UK male 200-metre sprinters in 2011

Identify any points which are outliers or influential points and make rough guesses of the correlation coefficients both including and excluding these points.

---

**Exercise 8**   *Investigating the tastiness of fruit*

An assessment of the tastiness of fruit, along with how easy they are to eat, is plotted on Figure 33 below. Assuming that these assessments provide a realistic comparison of fruit, answer the following questions.

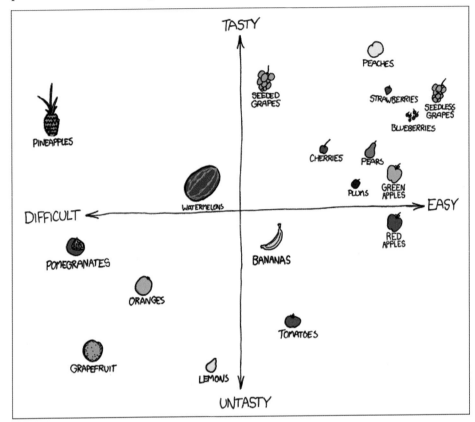

**Figure 33**   Taste versus difficulty in eating

(a) Do any fruits in Figure 33 appear to be outliers? Do any appear to be influential points? Justify your answers.

(b) After looking at Figure 33, one person said: 'So this means being easy to eat makes a fruit more tasty'. Is this person's conclusion appropriate?

# 4 Confidence intervals from $z$-tests

An important use of statistical methods is to make estimates. In our everyday lives we commonly give estimates in the form of intervals, such as 'the work will take me 30 to 40 minutes to do' or 'it will cost £50 to £60'. How such intervals should be interpreted is not always completely clear – is it certain that the work will take somewhere between 30 and 40 minutes, or simply very likely that it will be completed within that time? We next consider ways of giving estimates as intervals that have precise interpretations. In this section we obtain interval estimates that are related to $z$-tests – these are readily calculated without a computer. In Section 5 we consider interval estimates in the context of least squares regression, when a computer is generally used to calculate the intervals.

## 4.1 Estimating the population mean

In Section 5 of Unit 7 you were introduced to the one-sample $z$-test. The test is used to examine whether a population mean has a specified value, say $A$. It involves setting up the hypothesis that the population mean is equal to $A$, and then using sample data to decide whether or not to reject the hypothesis at the 5% significance level. If we do *not* reject the hypothesis, we conclude that the sample could well have come from a population with mean $A$; whereas if we *do* reject the hypothesis, we conclude that, based on the sample, the population mean is probably not equal to $A$.

In neither case do we say much about what the true value of $A$ is. The sample mean is an estimate of $A$, but often it would be helpful to have an interval that gives the range of values that $A$ might plausibly have. We shall obtain a method of constructing such an interval. The method is derived from the one-sample $z$-test.

In Section 1 of this unit we had a random sample of 100 English state secondary schools. The value of $P_{KS4}$ (the GCSE headline figure) was determined for each school. These values have a mean of 50.3 and a standard deviation of 17.19.

---

**Example 11**  *$z$-test of whether $P_{KS4}$ equals 45.0*

Suppose we want to test, at the 5% significance level, whether the mean value of $P_{KS4}$ in English state schools equals 45.0%.

Then we let $\mu$ denote the mean of $P_{KS4}$ in English state schools and set up the hypotheses

$H_0: \mu = 45.0$   and   $H_1: \mu \neq 45.0$.

The population standard deviation is unknown and the size is large (over 25), so the test statistic is

$$z = \frac{\overline{x} - A}{\text{ESE}}, \quad \text{where ESE} = \frac{s}{\sqrt{n}}.$$

Here, $A = 45.0$, $\bar{x} = 50.3$, $n = 100$ and $s = 17.19$. Hence,

$$z = \frac{50.3 - 45.0}{17.19/\sqrt{100}} \simeq 3.08.$$

The critical values for a $z$-test at the 5% significance level are $-1.96$ and $1.96$. As 3.08 is greater than 1.96, the null hypothesis is rejected at the 5% significance level. Thus there is moderate evidence that the mean value of $P_{KS4}$ is not 45.0%.

---

The hypothesis test enables us to conclude that the population mean is probably not equal to 45.0%, but it does not actually give an estimate for the mean. If we want to estimate the population mean by a single value, then the sample mean is the obvious choice, and it can give a good idea of what the population mean is likely to be. Estimates such as this, which consist of a single number, are called **point estimates**.

They are not entirely satisfactory as estimates because, without other information, we have no indication of their accuracy. A more satisfactory approach is to specify a range of likely values for the population mean, by finding two numbers between which the mean is likely to lie. We shall use the sample values to find these two numbers. Such a range of numbers is called an **interval** and is said to provide an **interval estimate** of the population mean.

In Subsection 4.2 we shall explore the most widely used form of interval estimate. It is called a **confidence interval** and it is based on many of the ideas that were introduced for hypothesis testing.

## 4.2   An interval estimate for the mean

We are now going to consider a whole series of hypothesis tests of the form

$$H_0: \mu = A \quad \text{and} \quad H_1: \mu \neq A.$$

In Example 11 (Subsection 4.1) we rejected the hypothesis that the population mean is equal to $A$ when we put $A = 45\%$. In Activity 16 you are asked to repeat the test for other values of $A$.

**Activity 16**   *z-test of whether $P_{KS4}$ equals 47.0, 53.0 and 55.0*

The mean and standard deviation of $P_{KS4}$ in a sample of 100 schools were equal to 50.3 and 17.19, respectively. Carry out separate one-sample $z$-tests at the 5% significance level for each of the following hypotheses.

(a)  The population mean is 47.0%.

(b)  The population mean is 53.0%.

(c)  The population mean is 55.0%.

In Activity 16 we tested the hypothesis $H_0: \mu = A$ for $A = 47.0$, $A = 53.0$ and $A = 55.0$. Following on from the activity, we might ask the question:

'What values of $A$ would be rejected in a test at the 5% significance level, and what values would we fail to reject?'

The question is important because we want an interval that contains the plausible values of $A$. For this, we might form the interval that consists of *those values of $A$ that are not rejected at the 5% significance level.* This interval is called the **95% confidence interval.** A 99% confidence interval is defined in a similar way, but using a 1% significance level in the hypothesis tests.

---

**Confidence intervals**

A 95% confidence interval for $\mu$ includes all values of $A$ for which we cannot reject $H_0$ at the 5% significance level.

A 99% confidence interval for $\mu$ includes all values of $A$ for which we cannot reject $H_0$ at the 1% significance level.

---

Performing lots of hypothesis tests seems a laborious way of determining a confidence interval, so we ask: *is there a straightforward way of finding confidence intervals for a population mean?*

Well, in Example 11 and Activity 16 the null hypothesis was rejected if (i) $z$ was greater than or equal to 1.96, or (ii) $z$ was less than or equal to $-1.96$. The value of $z$ was obtained by calculating

$$z = \frac{50.3 - A}{17.19/\sqrt{100}} = \frac{50.3 - A}{1.719}.$$

So when is the null hypothesis not rejected? It is not rejected by (i) if $z$ is less than 1.96, so when

$$\frac{50.3 - A}{1.719} < 1.96,$$

which implies

$$50.3 - A < 1.96 \times 1.719,$$

which in turn implies

$$50.3 - 1.96 \times 1.719 < A.$$

Similarly, it is not rejected by (ii) if $z$ is greater than $-1.96$, so when

$$-1.96 < \frac{50.3 - A}{1.719},$$

which implies

$$-1.96 \times 1.719 < 50.3 - A,$$

giving

$$A < 50.3 + 1.96 \times 1.719.$$

Thus the value of $A$ is rejected by neither (i) nor (ii) when

$$50.3 - 1.96 \times 1.719 < A < 50.3 + 1.96 \times 1.719,$$

that is, when (rounding to one decimal place)

$$46.9 < A < 53.7.$$

This gives the range of values for $A$ for which we do not reject the null hypothesis at the 5% significance level. Thus it is also our 95% confidence interval for the population mean. The interval consisting of all numbers from 46.9 to 53.7 is written

$$(46.9, 53.7).$$

So we would write that $(46.9\%, 53.7\%)$ is the 95% confidence interval for the mean $P_{KS4}$ in English state schools.

If a hypothesis is rejected at the 5% significance level, it means that the test statistic was one of the 5% most extreme values. Thus, if the null hypothesis is true, there is a probability of $1 - 0.05 = 0.95$ or 95% that the sample we select will *not* give a test statistic in one of the extreme tails of the distribution. This is the area we consider for our confidence interval, so this is why it is called a 95% confidence interval.

We could start with

$$z = \frac{\overline{x} - A}{s/\sqrt{n}} \quad \text{rather than} \quad z = \frac{50.3 - A}{17.19/\sqrt{100}}$$

and perform the same operations. We would find that a value of $A$ is rejected by neither (i) nor (ii) at the 5% significance level when

$$\overline{x} - 1.96 \times s/\sqrt{n} < A < \overline{x} + 1.96 \times s/\sqrt{n}.$$

This gives a procedure for calculating the 95% confidence interval for a population mean. Replacing 1.96 by 2.58 gives the 99% confidence interval.

### Calculating 95% and 99% confidence intervals for a population mean

Suppose the sample size is $n$, the sample mean is $\overline{x}$, and the sample standard deviation is $s$.

- Calculate the estimated standard error: $\text{ESE} = s/\sqrt{n}$.
- The 95% confidence interval for the population mean is
$$(\overline{x} - 1.96\,\text{ESE}, \ \overline{x} + 1.96\,\text{ESE}).$$
- The 99% confidence interval for the population mean is
$$(\overline{x} - 2.58\,\text{ESE}, \ \overline{x} + 2.58\,\text{ESE}).$$

As with the $z$-test, these formulas should only be used if the sample size is at least 25.

And here's the alternative formula . . .

**Example 12**   *Confidence interval for a population mean*

Suppose a sample of size 30 has a sample mean of 40.3 and a sample standard deviation of 2.3. Then

$$n = 30, \quad \bar{x} = 40.3 \quad \text{and} \quad s = 2.3.$$

We have $\text{ESE} = 2.3/\sqrt{30} \simeq 0.4199$.

A 95% confidence interval for the population mean is

$$(\bar{x} - 1.96 \, \text{ESE}, \ \bar{x} + 1.96 \, \text{ESE})$$
$$\simeq (40.3 - 1.96 \times 0.4199, 40.3 + 1.96 \times 0.4199)$$
$$\simeq (40.3 - 0.8230, 40.3 + 0.8230)$$
$$\simeq (39.5, 41.1).$$

Similarly, a 99% confidence interval for the population mean is

$$(\bar{x} - 2.58 \, \text{ESE}, \ \bar{x} + 2.58 \, \text{ESE})$$
$$\simeq (40.3 - 2.58 \times 0.4199, 40.3 + 2.58 \times 0.4199)$$
$$\simeq (40.3 - 1.0833, 40.3 + 1.0833)$$
$$\simeq (39.2, 41.4).$$

We round the numbers forming the confidence interval to the same level of accuracy as the sample mean.

**Activity 17**   *Calculating a confidence interval for a population mean*

Suppose a sample of size 50 has a sample mean of 15.62 and a sample standard deviation of 6.44.

(a)  Calculate a 95% confidence interval for the population mean.

(b)  Calculate a 99% confidence interval for the population mean.

**Activity 18**   *Calculating confidence intervals for jam*

For a sample of 37 jars of a particular manufacturer's plum jam, the sum of the weights (in grams) and the sum of the squares of the weights were as follows:

$$\sum x = 16\,946, \quad \sum x^2 = 7\,762\,644.$$

(a)  Calculate the mean and standard deviation of the weights in this sample.

(b)  Calculate a 95% confidence interval for the mean weight of jars of plum jam produced by this manufacturer.

**Activity 19**   *Which confidence interval is wider?*

If both a 95% confidence interval and a 99% confidence interval were calculated for a population mean, which would be wider?

## The interpretation of a confidence interval

We now have a way of finding a 95% confidence interval from a random sample, but we have not yet discussed how a confidence interval can be interpreted. Suppose we draw a very large number of different samples from some population with an unknown mean. Then although we do not know the value of the mean, from each sample we could form a confidence interval for it. Many of these confidence intervals will contain the population mean, but occasionally we will pick a sample that is not very representative of the population, and then the confidence interval might fail to contain it. For example, if we picked a random sample of twenty-five adults, we might by chance pick 24 men and only one woman. Then a confidence interval for, say, the population mean height might fail to contain the true mean height of all adults.

As a more specific example, suppose we pick a large number of samples of English state schools, each sample containing 100 schools. For each school we record the GCSE headline figure ($P_{KS4}$). We then calculate the mean and standard deviation of the 100 $P_{KS4}$ values we obtained in each sample. The following are what these statistics might look like for, say, the first eight samples.

- Sample 1: $\bar{x} = 53.0$, $s = 16.32$
- Sample 2: $\bar{x} = 49.6$, $s = 17.36$
- Sample 3: $\bar{x} = 49.0$, $s = 14.82$
- Sample 4: $\bar{x} = 51.9$, $s = 16.81$
- Sample 5: $\bar{x} = 50.4$, $s = 15.51$
- Sample 6: $\bar{x} = 52.1$, $s = 17.55$
- Sample 7: $\bar{x} = 54.8$, $s = 16.68$
- Sample 8: $\bar{x} = 50.9$, $s = 17.94$

For each sample, we can calculate a 95% confidence interval for the population mean. The formula for the interval is:

$$(\bar{x} - 1.96s/\sqrt{100}, \bar{x} + 1.96s/\sqrt{100}).$$

For the above eight samples, the 95% confidence intervals are:

- Sample 1: $(49.8\%, 56.2\%)$
- Sample 2: $(46.2\%, 53.0\%)$
- Sample 3: $(46.1\%, 51.9\%)$
- Sample 4: $(48.6\%, 55.2\%)$
- Sample 5: $(47.4\%, 53.4\%)$
- Sample 6: $(48.7\%, 55.5\%)$
- Sample 7: $(51.5\%, 58.1\%)$
- Sample 8: $(47.4\%, 54.4\%)$

Suppose, now, that the mean GCSE headline figure for English state schools is actually 51.0%. Then all but one of the above confidence intervals contain the true population mean. (The exception is Sample 7.)

In fact, if we had a very large number of samples, and calculated a 95% confidence interval from each of them, 95% of the confidence intervals would contain the population mean.

This leads to the following interpretation of a 95% confidence interval.

## Confidence intervals and the population mean

About 95% of the possible random samples we could select will give rise to a 95% confidence interval that *does* include the population mean.

Of the remaining intervals, half of them will be completely below the population mean, and the other half will be completely above the population mean. That is, about 2.5% will give intervals that are completely below the population mean and about 2.5% will give intervals completely above the population mean.

Thus, about 5% of possible random samples that might be selected will give rise to a 95% confidence interval that *does not* include the population mean.

So if you say that a 95% confidence interval includes the population mean, you will be right 95% of the time; that is, you can be 95% confident that your statement is correct.

Another way of thinking of a confidence interval is from the point of view of a working statistician who calculates 95% confidence intervals on many occasions. On about 95% of the occasions the interval will include the mean, but on the other 5% of occasions it will not.

An important point to note is the very close link between a hypothesis test and a confidence interval. A confidence interval contains the values that the population mean might plausibly equal, and the purpose of a hypothesis test is to reject implausible values. From the way we obtain the formula for a confidence interval, we have an exact link.

## Confidence intervals and hypothesis tests

If the confidence interval does include the hypothesised population mean, we do not reject the hypothesis. If the confidence interval does not include the hypothesised population mean, then we do reject the hypothesis. In particular:

- If the 95% confidence interval does not include the hypothesised population mean, then we reject the hypothesis at the 5% significance level.
- If the 99% confidence interval does not include the hypothesised population mean, then we reject the hypothesis at the 1% significance level.

**Activity 20**   *Doing hypothesis tests about jam*

In Activity 18, you calculated a 95% confidence interval for the mean weight of jars of plum jam produced by a particular manufacturer. Let $\mu$ be this mean weight. On the basis of your confidence interval, what can you say about the conclusion that would be drawn from each of the following hypothesis tests?

(a)  A hypothesis test of $H_0$: $\mu = 454$ against $H_1$: $\mu \neq 454$.

(b)  A hypothesis test of $H_0$: $\mu = 457$ against $H_1$: $\mu \neq 457$.

*You have now covered the material related to Screencasts 4 and 5 for Unit 9 (see the M140 website).*

## 4.3  An interval estimate for the difference between two means

We can also derive a confidence interval from two-sample $z$-tests (introduced in Section 6 of Unit 7). These tests are used when we have one sample from a population with mean $\mu_A$ and a second sample from a population with mean $\mu_B$. The hypothesis test examines whether these population means might be equal. The hypothesis test requires the two sample sizes to both be 25 or more. Provided this condition is satisfied, then the samples can also be used to form a confidence interval for the difference between the two population means, $\mu_A - \mu_B$.

As before, we obtain the confidence interval by trying various values of the quantity in which we are interested: in this case, $\mu_A - \mu_B$. As the sample sizes are large, we know that

$$z = \frac{(\bar{x}_A - \bar{x}_B) - (\mu_A - \mu_B)}{\mathrm{ESE}}$$

has approximately the standard normal distribution. The method for obtaining a confidence interval is to calculate $z$ for different values of $\mu_A - \mu_B$ and carry out a hypothesis test each time. If the null hypothesis is rejected for a particular value of $\mu_A - \mu_B$, then that value is not included in the confidence interval; otherwise it is included. This gives the following procedure.

Calculating 95% and 99% confidence intervals for $\mu_A - \mu_B$, the difference between two population means

Suppose the two sample sizes are $n_A$ and $n_B$, the sample means are $\overline{x}_A$ and $\overline{x}_B$, and the sample standard deviations are $s_A$ and $s_B$.

• Calculate the estimated standard error:

$$\text{ESE} = \sqrt{\frac{s_A^2}{n_A} + \frac{s_B^2}{n_B}}.$$

• The 95% confidence interval for $\mu_A - \mu_B$ is

$$(\overline{x}_A - \overline{x}_B - 1.96\,\text{ESE},\ \overline{x}_A - \overline{x}_B + 1.96\,\text{ESE}).$$

• The 99% confidence interval for $\mu_A - \mu_B$ is

$$(\overline{x}_A - \overline{x}_B - 2.58\,\text{ESE},\ \overline{x}_A - \overline{x}_B + 2.58\,\text{ESE}).$$

These formulas should only be used if the sample sizes are at least 25.

---

**Example 13**   *99% confidence interval estimate for $\mu_A - \mu_B$*

Activity 6 (Subsection 1.2) concerned the GCSE headline figures ($P_{\text{KS4}}$) in community schools compared with other schools. The data that were used to make the comparison were given in Table 2, reproduced here as Table 7.

**Table 7**   Summary statistics for $P_{\text{KS4}}$ by type of school

|  | Sample size | Sample mean (%) | Sample standard deviation (%) |
|---|---|---|---|
| Community school | 43 | 49.8 | 13.55 |
| Other school | 57 | 50.7 | 19.61 |

We will calculate a 99% confidence interval for $\mu_A - \mu_B$, where $\mu_A$ is the average GCSE headline figure in community schools, while $\mu_B$ is the average in other schools. We first calculate the ESE:

$$\text{ESE} = \sqrt{\frac{s_A^2}{n_A} + \frac{s_B^2}{n_B}} = \sqrt{\frac{13.55^2}{43} + \frac{19.61^2}{57}} \simeq 3.319.$$

Now

$$(\overline{x}_A - \overline{x}_B - 2.58\,\text{ESE},\ \overline{x}_A - \overline{x}_B + 2.58\,\text{ESE})$$
$$\simeq (49.8 - 50.7 - 2.58 \times 3.319,\ 49.8 - 50.7 + 2.58 \times 3.319)$$
$$\simeq (-0.9 - 8.56,\ -0.9 + 8.56)$$
$$\simeq (-9.5, 7.7).$$

So the 99% confidence interval for $\mu_A - \mu_B$ is $(-9.5\%, 7.7\%)$. Notice this includes zero. This was expected, as in Activity 6 we did not reject the null hypothesis that the difference between the population means was zero, so zero is a plausible value for the difference.

**Activity 21  *95% confidence interval estimate for $\mu_A - \mu_B$***

Calculate the 95% confidence interval for the difference between the average GCSE headline figure in community schools and the average GCSE headline figure in other schools.

**Activity 22  *Investigating the effect of siblings***

A researcher set out to investigate children's verbal skills at the age of six. She wished to compare the performance of only children (which she defined as children with no brothers or sisters, and not living in a household with other children) with that of children who live with at least one other child.

The researcher devised a short test, and gave it to two random samples of six-year-old children: one sample of only children and one sample of children, 'other' children, who live with at least one other child. The results are summarised in the following table.

|  | Sample size | Sample mean | Sample standard deviation |
| --- | --- | --- | --- |
| Only children ($A$) | 100 | 58.4 | 18.2 |
| Other children ($B$) | 150 | 52.1 | 20.6 |

Calculate a 95% confidence interval for the difference in average scores between only children and other children.

Suppose a hypothesis test were performed to compare the average scores of these two groups of children. On the basis of the confidence interval, what can be said about the conclusion that would be made from the test?

## Exercises on Section 4

**Exercise 9  *Quantifying the size of skulls***

In an investigation of skull size, the breadth of 30 male Egyptian skulls dating from around 4000 BC were measured. The mean and standard deviation of these measurements (in millimetres) were 131.4 and 5.1, respectively.

(a) Calculate a 95% confidence interval for the breadth of male Egyptian skulls of that period.

(b) If a 99% confidence interval were calculated, would it be wider or narrower than the interval that you calculated in (a)?

**Exercise 10**  *Measuring the changing size of skulls*

As part of the investigation described in Exercise 9, the breadth of 30 male Egyptian skulls from about 1850 BC were also measured. The sample mean was 134.5 mm, and the sample standard deviation was 3.4 mm.

Calculate a 95% confidence interval for the change in mean breadth of male Egyptian skulls from 4000 BC to 1850 BC. Has the mean breadth changed over that time?

# 5 Interval estimates from fitted lines

In the previous section you learned about interval estimates. In particular, you learned how to calculate and interpret confidence intervals for means. In this section you will learn about interval estimates in another context – least squares regression.

Recall that in Section 4 of Unit 5 we found that a linear relationship can be modelled by fitting a least squares regression line to the data. The line can be written in the form of the equation

$$y = a + bx,$$

where $a$ is the intercept of the line and $b$ is the slope of the line. The regression line can then be used to estimate the value of the dependent variable for a known value of the explanatory variable. The fitted value $y = a + bx$ is an estimate of the average value of $y$ when the explanatory variable has the value $x$.

So least squares regression lines can be used to make predictions. This is important, and leads to the following two types of interval estimate:

- The *confidence interval for the mean response*, which provides an interval for the position of the regression line. This is introduced in Subsection 5.1.

- The *prediction interval*, which provides an interval for the prediction of a new value. This is introduced in Subsection 5.2.

In Subsection 5.3, you will be referred to the Computer Book to explore confidence intervals further and learn how to produce these confidence intervals and prediction intervals using Minitab.

## 5.1   Confidence intervals for the mean response

In Subsection 3.1, Example 7 introduced some data on the pass rates in English and Mathematics. Suppose that $y$ represents the pass rate in Mathematics and $x$ represents the pass rate in English. Then the least squares fitted line for the data in Figure 17 of the example has the following equation:

$$y = 15.9 + 0.720x.$$

This line can be used to predict the pass rate in Mathematics when the pass rate in English is known. For example, for schools where the pass rate in English is 50%, the pass rate in Mathematics is estimated to be

$$15.9\% + 0.720 \times 50\% = 51.9\%.$$

This estimate of 51.9% is a single number, so it is a point estimate. Although a point estimate may be a 'best guess', it says nothing about what other values are also plausible. For this, an interval estimate is required.

In Section 4 you saw that a confidence interval for a mean can be calculated by thinking about the range of values which would not be rejected in a $z$-test. In this section we will take a slightly different, but related, approach to thinking about interval estimates – we will consider what might have happened if we had taken another sample. To do this we need to introduce the concept of a **population least squares regression line**. This is the regression line that we would calculate if we knew all values in the whole population for both variables, instead of just those in the sample we have observed.

$\alpha$ and $\beta$ are the first two letters of the Greek alphabet. $\alpha$ is 'alpha' and $\beta$ is 'beta'.

We shall write the equation of the population least squares regression line as $y = \alpha + \beta x$. The quantity $\beta$ is then the **population slope of the least squares regression line**, and $\alpha$ is the **population intercept of the least squares regression line**. The coefficients of the least squares regression line calculated from a sample are then just sample estimates of $\alpha$ and $\beta$. It is to be expected that the sample slope and the sample intercept will be close to these population values – but how close?

One way of exploring this is to think about what would happen if we took a number of separate samples from the population and calculated a least squares regression line for each sample. For example, suppose a population consists of 500 individuals, and the observations of two variables $x$ and $y$ on all 500 individuals were as follows.

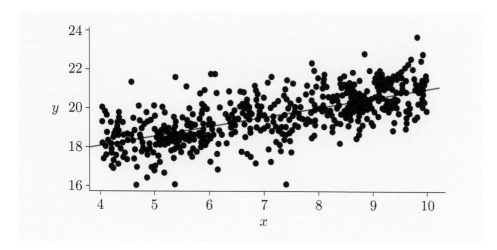

**Figure 34**   A scatterplot of data for a population of 500 individuals

For this population the relationship between $x$ and $y$ is positive, linear and reasonably strong. The least squares regression line summarising these data has the equation

$$y = 16.15 + 0.48x.$$

Now suppose a random sample of 20 individuals is taken from the population and the regression line given by the sample is calculated. One such sample, and the resulting regression line, is shown in Figure 35.

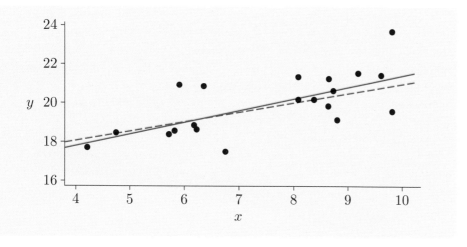

**Figure 35**   A scatterplot of data for a sample of 20 individuals. The solid line gives the least squares regression line based on the sample. The dashed line gives the least squares regression line for the population

The equation of the regression line for this sample is

$$y = 15.42 + 0.603x.$$

So for this sample, the intercept happens to be a bit lower than the correct value for the whole population, and the slope turns out to be a bit higher. Overall, the regression line for the sample is below the population line for values of $x$ that are less than 6, and above the population line for $x$-values that are greater than 6.

If other samples are taken, the position of the regression line will differ from sample to sample, fluctuating around the regression line given by the whole population. This is illustrated in Figure 36, where regression lines from 100 different random samples (each of size 20) are shown.

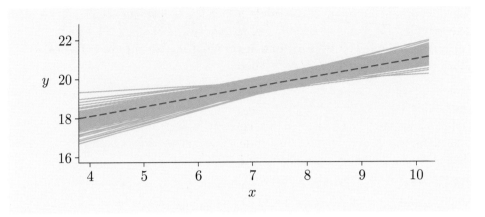

**Figure 36**   Regression lines calculated using 100 different samples of 20 individuals. The solid lines are the regression lines from the samples. The dashed line gives the regression line for the population

Notice that the question of which sample lines are most extreme depends on the value of $x$ being considered. Different lines are the most extreme ones for different values of $x$.

To clarify the variability in the lines, we could plot, for every value of $x$, the band within which 95% of the sample lines lie. This is done, in Figure 37, for the population of 500 individuals shown in Figure 34. The band is wider towards the ends of the range of $x$ than at the centre of the range, and symmetrical about the population regression line.

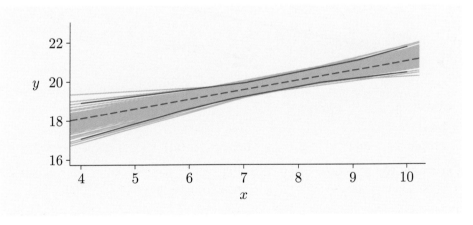

**Figure 37**   Least squares regression lines calculated using 100 different samples of 20 individuals. The solid curves delineate the band within which 95% of the sample least squares regression lines lie for each value of $x$. The dashed line gives the least squares regression line for the population

Figure 37 characterises the differences between the population regression line and the sample regression lines. Usually, of course, we only have the regression line from one sample, rather than a regression line from each of

100 samples. We would like to use that sample regression line to estimate the plausible points that the population regression line might pass through.

How might this be achieved? The approach usually taken is to make assumptions about how points are scattered around the population line. This enables statements to be made about the population line using just one sample of points. In particular, for any value of the explanatory variable $x$, it allows a **confidence interval for the mean value of** $y$ (the 'mean response') to be constructed.

Now suppose we are given a confidence interval for the mean response for a particular value of $x$, the interval $(y_{\min}, y_{\max})$. If we happened to know the population slope and intercept, we could also calculate what the 'correct' answer is, say $y_{\text{true}}$. Then our confidence interval either contains $y_{\text{true}}$ or it does not. And it would be helpful if it did.

(In practice we do not know the population slope and intercept. If we did, there would be no point working with the sample values.)

It is not possible to construct a useful interval from sample data that is guaranteed to always contain $y_{\text{true}}$. Instead the confidence interval $(y_{\min}, y_{\max})$ is constructed in such a way that there is a high chance it will contain $y_{\text{true}}$. Typically this 'high chance' is taken to be a probability of 95%, so the 95% confidence interval for the mean response is formed. That is, with 100 such intervals, on average 95 of them will contain $y_{\text{true}}$. So given just one interval, saying that it contains $y_{\text{true}}$ is the right thing to say 95% of the time.

Dickens's Scrooge: someone capable of a mean response!

(GARFIELD © 1999 Paws, Inc. Reprinted with permission of UNIVERSAL UCLICK. All rights reserved.)

---

**Example 14**  *Interpreting a confidence interval for the mean response*

Returning to the sample plotted in Figure 35, the 95% confidence interval for the mean response when $x = 8$ turns out to be (19.67, 20.82).

This means that there is a 95% chance that the statement 'The interval (19.67, 20.82) contains the (population) mean value of $y$ when $x = 8$' is true.

---

**Activity 23**   *Interpreting another confidence interval*

Using the population line, calculate the population mean of $y$ when $x = 6$. Is the statement 'The interval $(18.31, 19.77)$ contains the (population) mean value of $y$ when $x = 6$' true or false?

**Activity 24**   *Interpreting yet another confidence interval*

From a different population, 100 samples were taken. For each sample, the confidence interval for the mean response was calculated for $x = 7$. These confidence intervals are plotted in Figure 38. The population least squares line was also determined and gives a value $y = 18.55$ when $x = 7$. The line corresponding to this value of $y$ is also plotted. In Figure 38 how many of the confidence intervals do not contain the population mean value of $y$? Hence what is the probability that a randomly chosen confidence interval out of these 100 intervals does include the population mean value?

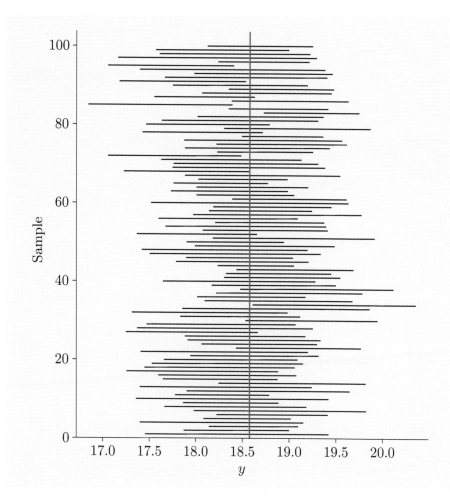

**Figure 38** Confidence intervals for the mean response when $x = 7$ for 100 different samples

**Activity 25** *Interpreting a confidence interval for a mean pass rate*

For schools with a pass rate in English of 50%, the predicted pass rate in Mathematics is 51.9%. The 95% confidence interval for the mean response turns out to be 48.6% to 55.2%. Interpret this confidence interval.

For any sample, it is possible to map the resulting confidence intervals for the mean response for a range of different $x$-values. For example, in Figure 39 the confidence intervals for a range of different values of $x$ are plotted. Notice that these confidence intervals have different widths, narrower in the centre, and wider as you move away from the centre.

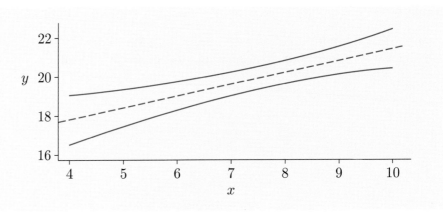

**Figure 39**   Limits of the 95% confidence intervals for the mean response (solid curves) based on one sample. The dotted line gives the least squares regression line based on the same sample

This pattern mirrors what you saw in Figure 37 and reflects two properties of confidence intervals for the mean response, as follows.

**Properties of the confidence interval for the mean response**

1.   Confidence intervals for the mean response are at their narrowest when $x$ is the sample mean, and get steadily wider each side.

2.   The least squares regression line based on the sample data is always in the middle of the interval. Hence the point estimate for the predicted value is always in the middle of the confidence interval for the mean response.

**Example 15**   *Deducing a point estimate from a confidence interval*

In Activity 25, a 95% confidence interval for the mean pass rate in Mathematics was 48.6% to 55.2% for schools with a pass rate in English of 50%.

The midpoint of this interval is $(48.6\% + 55.2\%)/2 = 51.9\%$. This is the same as the predicted pass rate in Mathematics for such schools.

**Activity 26**   *Comparing widths of confidence intervals*

The width of the confidence interval given in Activity 25 is $55.2\% - 48.6\% = 6.6\%$. Confidence intervals for various pass rates in English are given in Table 8.

**Table 8**  Some confidence intervals for the mean pass rate in Mathematics

| Pass rate in English | Confidence interval for mean pass rate in Mathematics | Width of confidence interval |
|---|---|---|
| 40 | (40.1%, 49.3%) | |
| 50 | (48.6%, 55.2%) | 6.6% |
| 60 | (56.9%, 61.3%) | |
| 70 | (64.5%, 68.1%) | |
| 80 | (71.0%, 75.9%) | |

(a)  Complete the final column of Table 8.

(b)  From Table 8, which confidence interval is narrowest? State the average pass rate in English to the nearest 10%.

## 5.2  Prediction intervals

In Subsection 5.1, interval estimates bracketing the position of the population line were introduced. However, for a given value of the explanatory variable, these intervals only indicate a range for the population mean – not a range for an individual value. Even if we know the exact position of the population line, that will not allow us to pinpoint where an individual point lies. Some individuals will be above the population line, whilst others will be below the population line. So for predictions about individuals, a different interval is required – a so-called **prediction interval**.

---

**Example 16**  *Prediction of a pass rate for a particular school*

In Activity 25 (Subsection 5.1) the confidence interval for the mean pass rate in Mathematics for schools with a pass rate of 50% in English was given as 48.6% to 55.2%.

Now, not all schools with a pass rate in English of 50% will have the same pass rate in Mathematics. Some will have a higher pass rate than the average, whilst others will not have quite as good a pass rate. So the interval 48.6% to 55.2% does not give a sufficient reflection of the variability in Mathematics pass rates between individual schools. A prediction interval takes such variability into account. For schools with a pass rate in English of 50%, the 95% prediction interval turns out to be 33.6% to 70.3%. So whilst on average such schools will have a pass rate in Mathematics of about 50%, for some schools the pass rate will be much higher, and for others it will be much lower.

---

## Prediction intervals

Prediction intervals reflect the random variation of individual values around the population regression line, as well as uncertainty about the actual position of that line. If we have a very large sample, then we will have a good idea about the position of the population regression line – most of the uncertainty in predicting the value of an individual will stem from the scatter of individual values about the regression line.

95% prediction intervals are calculated so that 95% of them will contain the actual value a new observation would take.

## Properties of prediction intervals

Prediction intervals inherit many of the properties of the confidence intervals for the mean response. In particular, a prediction interval:

- is centred around the predicted value $a + bx$
- is narrowest when $x$ is the sample mean, and steadily widens away from this point
- gets wider as the scatter around the line increases.

Also, a prediction interval is always wider than the corresponding confidence interval for the mean response.

**Activity 27**   *Valid prediction interval?*

For a school with a pass rate in English of 35%, the 95% confidence interval for the mean response is 35.9% to 46.4%. Two different students quote the corresponding prediction interval. Ali says the interval is 37.8% to 44.5%, and Charlie says the interval is 17.3% to 55.0%.

Explain why both Ali and Charlie must be mistaken.

*You have now covered the material related to Screencast 6 for Unit 9 (see the M140 website).*

## 5.3   Computer work: interval estimates

In Sections 4 and 5 you have been introduced to various interval estimates. Although you have learned how to calculate some of these intervals, the emphasis has been on the interpretation of the intervals. In this subsection you will learn how to use Minitab to obtain various interval estimates. You will learn how to produce confidence intervals for the mean based on the one-sample z-test, and how to obtain confidence intervals for the mean response and prediction intervals. You will also further explore the confidence intervals for the mean response.

In M140, you will not be expected to calculate confidence intervals for the mean response or prediction intervals by hand.

You should now turn to the Computer Book and work through Subsection 9.1 if you have not already done so, followed by the rest of Chapter 9.

## Exercises on Section 5

**Exercise 11**   *Predicting the effect of a drug*

In Subsection 3.3 of Unit 5, some data on the effect of a drug, captopril, were introduced. The data consisted of diastolic blood pressure measurements before, and two hours after, injection with captopril for 15 patients. Using those data the following least squares line was calculated:

$$y = 4.2 + 0.880x,$$

where $y$ is a patient's diastolic blood pressure two hours after injection with captopril, and $x$ is the patient's diastolic blood pressure before the injection.

(a) Using the least squares regression line, calculate the diastolic blood pressure two hours after the injection for patients with an initial diastolic blood pressure of 110 mmHg. Why might an interval estimate be preferred?

(b) The 95% confidence interval for the mean post-injection diastolic blood pressure is 95.9 to 106.1 mmHg. Does this suggest that captopril is effective in reducing blood pressure in patients with an initial diastolic blood pressure of 110 mmHg? (Here, take 'effective' to mean that the diastolic blood pressure is, on average, reduced.)

(c) Does the confidence interval given in part (b) suggest that for any particular patient with an initial diastolic blood pressure of 110 mmHg, captopril is likely to be effective?

Exercise 3 (Section 2) showed the best times for the 200-metre and 100-metre sprints by UK male sprinters in 2011.

A few UK male sprinters only had a time recorded for the 200-metre sprint. Using a least squares regression line, it is possible to predict a time for the 100-metre sprint that these sprinters might have achieved in 2011.

(a)  For one such sprinter, the 95% prediction interval for his best 100-metre time in 2011 is 9.88 seconds to 10.62 seconds. Interpret the meaning of this interval.

(b)  What must have been the point estimate associated with the prediction interval given in part (a)?

(c)  The 'B' standard qualifying time for the men's 100 metres at the 2012 Olympics was 10.24 seconds. Is it plausible that the sprinter in part (a) could have achieved this qualifying time? Why or why not?

(d)  Figure 40 is a scatterplot of the best times for the 200-metre sprint and 100-metre sprint achieved in 2011 for 100 UK sprinters, along with the 95% prediction intervals. On the plot, the points that lie below the 95% prediction interval and the points that lie above the 95% prediction interval are marked with different symbols. Based on this, do the prediction intervals look reasonable? Justify your answer.

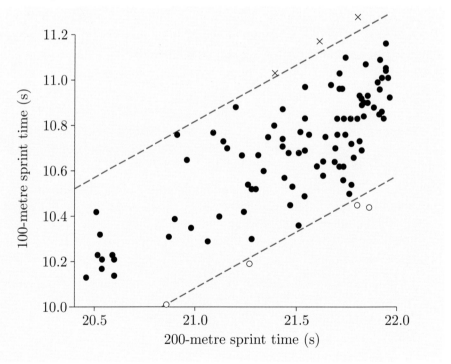

**Figure 40**   Times for male UK sprinters in 2011 with 95% prediction intervals

# 6 Case study

In Section 1, we began measuring the quality of an English secondary school using the GCSE headline figure ($P_{\mathrm{KS4}}$) – the percentage of students at the end of Key Stage 4 who achieve at least five A* to C grade GCSEs including English and Mathematics. Performance in GCSEs relates both to characteristics of the school and characteristics of the students. A school that attracts academically able students and then teaches them poorly could have a higher GCSE headline figure than a school that attracts academically less able students and then teaches them well. Hence, in assessing a school's performance, some account should perhaps be taken of students' academic ability when they started at the school. The purpose of this case study is to explore one possible way of doing this.

In Subsection 1.2, a measure of the academy ability of eleven-year-old students was introduced: $P_{\mathrm{KS2}}$ – the average points score of students at the end of Key Stage 2. As the end of Key Stage 2 is the end of primary education, $P_{\mathrm{KS2}}$ only indicates the ability of a secondary school's intake, not any impact of the secondary school's teaching. We are focusing on the $P_{\mathrm{KS4}}$ of 100 secondary schools in 2011. The cohort of students taking GCSEs in 2011 took Key Stage 2 tests in 2006. The Key Stage 2 average point score of a school's intake in 2006 will be referred to as its $P_{\mathrm{KS2}}$. As with $P_{\mathrm{KS4}}$, a higher value of $P_{\mathrm{KS2}}$ indicates that the students were on average doing better in national examinations. Here we consider using $P_{\mathrm{KS2}}$ to predict $P_{\mathrm{KS4}}$, and examine whether taking account of $P_{\mathrm{KS2}}$ would change perception of which schools perform well.

**Activity 28**   *Describing the relationship between $P_{KS2}$ and $P_{KS4}$*

A scatterplot of the Key Stage 2 results and the Key Stage 4 results for
each of the 100 schools is given in Figure 41.

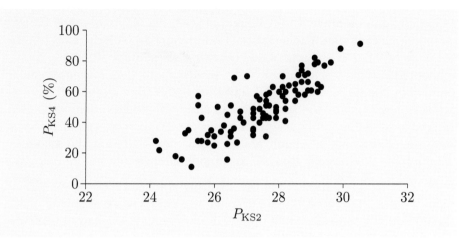

**Figure 41**   Scatterplot of $P_{KS4}$ and $P_{KS2}$

(a) Describe the relationship between $P_{KS4}$ and $P_{KS2}$.

(b) Is the correlation coefficient likely to be a good guide to the strength
    of the relationship between $P_{KS4}$ and $P_{KS2}$? Why or why not?

(c) Are there any outliers or influential points? Justify your answer.

(d) The correlation coefficient turns out to be $+0.83$. Does this make sense
    in the light of your answer to part (a)?

As noted in Activity 28, the relationship between $P_{KS2}$ and $P_{KS4}$ appears
to be reasonably linear. So the relationship between the two variables can
be summarised by a straight line with $P_{KS4}$ as the response variable and
$P_{KS2}$ as the explanatory variable.

**Activity 29**   *Modelling Key Stage 4 results*

Calculate the equation of the least squares regression line using the data
from the 100 non-selective schools depicted in Figure 41, giving the slope
to three decimal places and the intercept to two decimal places. (The
calculation of the least squares regression line was introduced in
Subsection 4.2 of Unit 5.) To reduce the amount of computation involved,
the first step of the calculation has already been completed for you:

$$\sum x = 2743.6, \quad \sum y = 5031,$$
$$\sum x^2 = 75\,449.44, \quad \sum y^2 = 282\,359, \quad \sum xy = 139\,903.0.$$

The least squares regression line, along with the 95% confidence interval for the mean response, is shown in Figure 42.

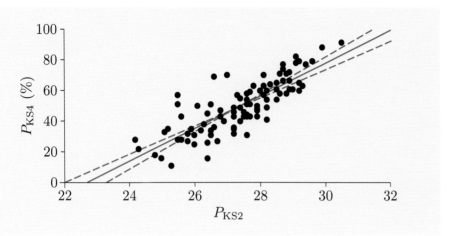

**Figure 42**   Least squares regression line and 95% confidence interval for the regression of $P_{KS4}$ on $P_{KS2}$

## Activity 30   *Interpreting the model*

Using Figure 42, give ranges for the mean GCSE headline figure for the following values of $P_{KS2}$. (As you are reading off a graph, all the numbers are expected to be approximate.)

(a)  24

(b)  28

(c)  30

From Figure 42, notice that values between the confidence limits all indicate a positive relationship between Key Stage 2 and Key Stage 4 results.

## Activity 31   *Measuring the relationship between Key Stage results*

Use the values given in Activity 29 to verify the value of the correlation coefficient between the Key Stage 2 and Key Stage 4 results given in Activity 28.

**Activity 32    *Comparing schools – 1***

Table 9 gives the GCSE headline figure and the Key Stage 2 average point score for each of three schools.

**Table 9**    Results for three schools

| School | Key Stage 2 | Key Stage 4 |
|--------|-------------|-------------|
| A | 29.3 | 63% |
| B | 28.1 | 57% |
| C | 25.5 | 51% |

(a)  Using the least squares regression line that you calculated in Activity 29, predict the results at Key Stage 4 for each school on the basis of their Key Stage 2 results. (Give your answers to one decimal place.)

Residuals were introduced in Subsection 3.2 of Unit 5.

(b)  For each school, calculate the residual. That is, calculate the residuals between the actual Key Stage 4 results and the predicted ones. Rank the schools on the basis of these residuals. Hence comment on the relative quality of education at the schools, as measured by the Key Stage results.

As you have seen in the last couple of activities, a least squares regression line can be used to predict the results a school will get at Key Stage 4 given the ability of its intake at Key Stage 2. However, as you learned in Section 5, by itself a point estimate conveys insufficient information. Also important is some indication of how accurate that estimate is.

For the three schools described in Activity 32 the prediction intervals are as follows.

**Table 10**    Prediction intervals for three schools

| School | Key Stage 2 | Key Stage 4 | Prediction | Prediction interval |
|--------|-------------|-------------|------------|---------------------|
| A | 29.3 | 63% | 70.1% | $(50.5\%, 89.8\%)$ |
| B | 28.1 | 57% | 57.4% | $(37.9\%, 76.9\%)$ |
| C | 25.5 | 51% | 29.7% | $(10.1\%, 49.4\%)$ |

Look at School A. As noted in Activity 32, 63% of its pupils achieved the Key Stage 4 benchmark in 2011, whilst a figure of just over 70% was expected on the basis of its intake. However, 63% is inside the prediction interval. So, on the basis of this model, just 63% achieving the benchmark is not exceptional.

'We were finding it impossible to get the kids into a decent school, so we had them adopted.'

**Activity 33**   *Comparing schools – 2*

Use the prediction intervals given in Table 10 to comment on the performance of schools B and C in 2011.

An overall picture of the prediction intervals is given in Figure 43. As in Figure 40 (in Exercises for Section 5), the schools whose GCSE headline figure lies outside the corresponding prediction interval are indicated using different plotting symbols. There were six such schools.

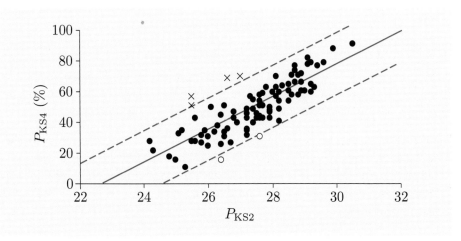

**Figure 43**   Least squares regression line and 95% prediction interval for the regression of $P_{KS4}$ on $P_{KS2}$

| Activity 34 | *Judging the model* |

Does Figure 43 indicate that the model is not correct?

| Activity 35 | *Comparing school performance measures* |

Consider the six schools that are outside the 95% prediction interval in Figure 43. If the Key Stage 2 results are ignored, is their performance at Key Stage 4 notable?

We have seen that the Key Stage 2 results can be used to predict the percentage of students who should get at least five A* to C grade GCSEs including English and Mathematics. Comparing this with the actual percentage gives a measure of the performance of the schools that allows for the ability of its students when they started at the school. Thus it provides a value-added measure of school performance that is an indication of how much the school has enhanced the ability of its students.

However, there are drawbacks to this approach. In this section we have been considering a line based on the data from just 100 secondary schools. Using information from more schools would improve the estimate. For example, a model could be fitted to all the data from 2011. But what about other years? A judgement would have to be taken as to whether it is reasonable to believe that the relationship between $P_{KS2}$ and $P_{KS4}$ is the same in other years as well.

We have only considered a linear relationship between $P_{KS2}$ and $P_{KS4}$. From Figure 41 this assumption looks reasonable. However, other more complicated relationships might fit the data better and lead to different predictions. These differences are likely to be only small, but small differences can be important if great emphasis is placed on this measure of school performance. Furthermore, we have only looked at using $P_{KS2}$ to predict $P_{KS4}$. Perhaps another measure is better. For example, ability at Key Stage 2 could be measured by just taking the results in English and Mathematics, and/or by considering the percentage who attain at least Level 4 (the expected standard at Key Stage 2) instead of the average point score. Also, should other factors about the school be taken into account – for example, the percentage of students from a disadvantaged background?

It must also be remembered that $P_{KS4}$ is only one measure of secondary school performance. Even if exam results are seen as the be all and end all of school education, it is arguable whether $P_{KS4}$ is the right measure. Should the range of grades be extended to A* to G instead of just A* to C? Should the range of qualifications include just English and Mathematics? Should it include more subjects? Changing the summary measure of attainment at Key Stage 4 will change the apparent performance of some schools.

Finally, with a lot potentially riding on a school's position relative to other schools, it is important that the means by which the performance is calculated is open, transparent and not subject to dispute. This requirement provides one explanation as to why league tables of school performance in 2011 chose only to focus on results at Key Stage 4, and not make any adjustment for the students' ability when they started at the school, though of course this might not be popular with schools who have a low-attaining intake.

## Exercises on Section 6

**Exercise 13**  *Predicting $P_{KS4}$ for selective schools*

In Section 6 we only used data for non-selective secondary schools. One question, therefore, is to what extent the model also works for selective schools (that is, schools where the admissions policy includes selection on the basis of ability).

(a) For the intake of some selective schools, $P_{KS2} = 31.0$. Calculate the predicted value of $P_{KS4}$ for these schools using the least squares regression line you calculated in Activity 29.

(b) The 95% confidence interval for the predicted value you calculated in part (a) is 82.7% to 93.8%. Interpret the meaning of this interval.

(c) In 2011, the highest value of $P_{KS2}$ for a selective school is given as 33.5. For such a school, the predicted value of $P_{KS4}$ is 114.8%, and the 95% prediction interval is 93.4% to 136.2%. The actual value of $P_{KS4}$ turned out to be 100%. Do the predicted value and prediction interval seem reasonable for such schools?

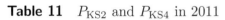

**Exercise 14**  *Exploring some data about selective schools*

The values of $P_{KS2}$ and $P_{KS4}$ for 15 selective English secondary schools are given in Table 11.

**Table 11**  $P_{KS2}$ and $P_{KS4}$ in 2011

| School | $P_{KS2}$ | $P_{KS4}$ (%) | School | $P_{KS2}$ | $P_{KS4}$ (%) |
|--------|-----------|---------------|--------|-----------|---------------|
| 1 | 33.4 | 100 | 9 | 32.8 | 99 |
| 2 | 30.9 | 95 | 10 | 31.8 | 97 |
| 3 | 33.0 | 100 | 11 | 32.2 | 100 |
| 4 | 32.6 | 99 | 12 | 32.7 | 100 |
| 5 | 33.5 | 100 | 13 | 33.1 | 100 |
| 6 | 32.2 | 99 | 14 | 30.9 | 91 |
| 7 | 31.3 | 95 | 15 | 31.4 | 100 |
| 8 | 32.1 | 98 | | | |

(a) Calculate the correlation coefficient between $P_{KS2}$ and $P_{KS4}$ using the data in Table 11.

(b)  A scatterplot of the data given in Table 11 is shown in Figure 44.

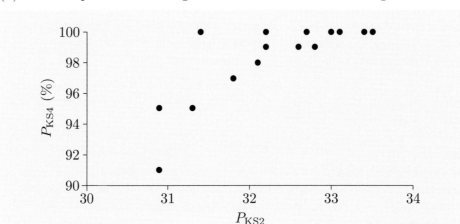

**Figure 44**   $P_{KS2}$ and $P_{KS4}$ for 15 selective secondary schools in England in 2011

Is the correlation coefficient you calculated in part (a) a good summary of the strength of the relationship between $P_{KS2}$ and $P_{KS4}$? Why or why not?

# Summary

In this unit the correlation coefficient was introduced – a quantity that measures the strength of a linear relationship between two variables. The correlation coefficient takes values between −1 and +1. When there is an exact positive relationship, the correlation coefficient takes a value of +1; when there is an exact negative relationship, the correlation coefficient takes a value of −1; and when there is no relationship, the correlation coefficient is zero.

You have learned how to calculate the correlation coefficient by hand and by using Minitab. When calculating the correlation coefficient, it does not matter which variable is treated as the explanatory variable, or how the variable is scaled. Outliers will tend to make the correlation coefficient appear too small, while influential points will tend to make the correlation coefficient appear too large.

You have also learned about interval estimates. In general they consist of intervals for population quantities, such as a mean or difference between means. Intervals are constructed in such a way that a known percentage of them contain the true value of the quantity of interest.

Confidence intervals for the population mean, $\mu$, are linked to $z$-tests. For one sample, a 95% confidence interval for $\mu$ includes all values for which we cannot reject $H_0$ at the 5% significance level. When there are two samples, a 95% confidence interval includes all the values for the difference between two means that we cannot reject at the 5% significance level. 99% confidence intervals have similar definitions and are wider than the corresponding 95% intervals. You have learned how to calculate such confidence intervals by hand.

Confidence intervals for the mean response are linked to the least squares regression line. They indicate intervals for the position of the population regression line for particular values of the explanatory variable. Prediction intervals are also linked to the least squares regression line. They provide an interval for the predicted value for an individual. Prediction intervals are wider than confidence intervals for the mean response, because even if the position of the line were known, there would still be uncertainty about the value taken by an individual item. You have learned how to obtain confidence intervals for the mean response and prediction intervals using Minitab.

Finally, you have used correlation coefficients and interval estimates to explore the quality of schools – in particular, to investigate how the GCSE headline score depends on other aspects of secondary schools. Thus you have gone some way to answering the questions: *What factors influence the quality of a school?* and *How good is a school?*

# Learning outcomes

After working through this unit, you should be able to:

- understand the concept of the correlation coefficient – in particular, how it relates to a relationship between two variables shown on a scatterplot
- calculate the correlation coefficient by hand
- calculate the correlation coefficient using Minitab
- roughly estimate a correlation coefficient from a scatterplot
- recognise outliers and influential points on a scatterplot, and understand their impact on the correlation coefficient
- calculate a confidence interval for a population mean
- interpret a confidence interval
- calculate a confidence interval for the difference between two population means
- interpret a confidence interval for estimating the mean response using a least squares regression line
- interpret a prediction interval for individual predictions from a least squares regression line
- obtain confidence intervals and prediction intervals for estimates from a least squares regression line using Minitab.

# Solutions to activities

### Solution to Activity 1

Most people would probably agree that a good school is one that provides a good education for all its students. However, what is meant by a good education is not simple to define. Enabling students to gain knowledge and skills is part of it. But you also may have thought of other aspects such as allowing students to develop artistic or sporting interests or having a positive ethos.

### Solution to Activity 2

The academic ability of a student can be measured by assessing the student. This assessment might be a formal exam, a test taken in the classroom, project work, or a teacher's assessment of work done in class or of work done at home. Also, the assessment might be on a narrow range of subjects, such as English, Mathematics and Science. Or the assessment could include a much wider range of subjects

### Solution to Activity 3

Using our definition of the quality of a school, the higher a school's GCSE headline figure ($P_{KS4}$), the better it is. However, what has not yet been defined is how high $P_{KS4}$ needs to be for the school to be 'good'. So it is not possible to say whether this school is good or not good.

### Solution to Activity 4

The histogram shows the variation between schools. For some schools $P_{KS4}$ is more than 80%, whereas for other schools $P_{KS4}$ is less than 30%. The median $P_{KS4}$ is somewhere between 40% and 60%. The distribution is roughly symmetric.

### Solution to Activity 5

(a) From Table 1, the number of schools with a $P_{KS4}$ of less than 50% is $4 + 8 + 17 + 22 = 51$. So, using the criterion $P_{KS4} \geq 50\%$, 51 schools in the sample would be deemed not good enough.

(b) From Table 1, the number of schools with a $P_{KS4}$ of less than 30% is $4 + 8 = 12$. So, using the criterion $P_{KS4} \geq 30\%$, 12 schools in the sample would be deemed not good enough.

(c) From Table 1, all but one of the schools had a value of $P_{KS4}$ less than 90%. So, using the criterion $P_{KS4} \geq 90\%$, 99 schools in the sample would be deemed not good enough.

## Solution to Activity 6

Let 'C' denote quantities relating to community schools, and let 'O' denote quantities relating to 'other' schools.

The null and alternative hypotheses are

$H_0$: $\mu_C = \mu_O$

$H_1$: $\mu_C \neq \mu_O$,

where $\mu_C$ and $\mu_O$ are the population means of $P_{KS4}$ of interest.

We have:

$$\overline{x}_C = 49.8 \quad \overline{x}_O = 50.7 \quad n_C = 43 \quad n_O = 57$$
$$s_C = 13.55 \quad s_O = 19.61.$$

Note that both $n_C$ and $n_O$ are greater than 25, so we can assume that the $z$-test is applicable.

The estimated standard error is

$$\text{ESE} = \sqrt{\frac{s_C^2}{n_C} + \frac{s_O^2}{n_O}} = \sqrt{\frac{13.55^2}{43} + \frac{19.61^2}{57}} \simeq 3.319,$$

and

$$z = \frac{\overline{x}_C - \overline{x}_O}{\text{ESE}} \simeq \frac{49.8 - 50.7}{3.319} \simeq -0.27.$$

The critical values are 1.96, $-1.96$ (5%) and 2.58, $-2.58$ (1%). Since $-1.96 < -0.27 < 1.96$, we cannot reject the null hypothesis at the 5% level. There is little evidence that the mean $P_{KS4}$ in community schools is different from its mean value in other schools.

## Solution to Activity 7

In Figure 3, the relationship between the variables is weak. At best the points only loosely follow a line.

In Figure 4, the relationship between the variables is strong. It is possible to draw a straight line such that all the points lie close to the line.

The relationship in Figure 5 is difficult to classify as strong or weak. It is weaker than the relationship in Figure 4 and stronger than the relationship in Figure 3. But whether this makes the relationship strong or weak is down to individual judgement.

### Solution to Activity 8

In (a), there is a strong positive relationship between the variables. The actual correlation coefficient is 0.92, but anything between 0.8 and just under 1.0 is a good guess. Remember that correlation coefficients always lie between $-1$ and $+1$, so you should not have guessed a number larger than 1.

The relationship in (b) is negative, but it is not as strong as in the first example; the points do not lie as close to a straight line. In this case, $r = -0.64$, but any guess between $-0.8$ and $-0.4$ would be reasonable.

In (c) there is only a weak relationship between the variables, but it is definitely positive. The actual value of the coefficient is 0.30.

### Solution to Activity 9

(a) For each constituency, let $x$ represent the attainment at Key Stage 2, and let $y$ represent the attainment at Key Stage 4.

1.  The five initial sums are as follows:
    $$\sum x = 508.0, \quad \sum y = 355.6,$$
    $$\sum x^2 = 37\,008.1, \quad \sum y^2 = 18\,600.62, \quad \sum xy = 26\,030.33.$$

2.  The sum of squared residuals of the $x$-values, the sum of squared residuals of the $y$-values and the sum of products of the residuals of the $x$- and $y$-values are as follows:
    $$\sum(x - \bar{x})^2 = 37\,008.1 - \frac{508.0^2}{7}$$
    $$\simeq 37\,008.1 - 36\,866.285\,71 = 141.814\,29,$$
    $$\sum(y - \bar{y})^2 = 18\,600.62 - \frac{355.6^2}{7}$$
    $$= 18\,600.62 - 18\,064.48 = 536.14,$$
    $$\sum(x - \bar{x})(y - \bar{y}) = 26\,030.33 - \frac{508.0 \times 355.6}{7}$$
    $$= 26\,030.33 - 25\,806.4 = 223.93.$$

3.  We can now calculate the correlation coefficient using the quantities calculated in step 2.
    $$r = \frac{\sum(x - \bar{x})(y - \bar{y})}{\sqrt{\sum(x - \bar{x})^2 \times \sum(y - \bar{y})^2}}$$
    $$\simeq \frac{223.93}{\sqrt{141.814\,29 \times 536.14}} \simeq \frac{223.93}{275.739\,58}$$
    $$\simeq 0.812\,11.$$

    So, the correlation coefficient for these data is 0.81 (rounded to two decimal places).

(b) In Figure 11 there is a clear positive relationship between the attainment at Key Stage 2 in 2006 and attainment at Key Stage 4 in 2011. Furthermore, this relationship looks reasonably linear. A correlation coefficient of +0.81 reflects this strong positive linear relationship.

## Solution to Activity 10

The information given in the question means we can start at step 2.

$$\sum(x-\overline{x})^2 = 2329 - \frac{135^2}{8} = 2329 - 2278.125 = 50.875.$$

$$\sum(y-\overline{y})^2 = 226 - \frac{40^2}{8} = 226 - 200 = 26.$$

$$\sum(x-\overline{x})(y-\overline{y}) = 708 - \frac{135 \times 40}{8} = 708 - 675 = 33.$$

Thus (using step 3) the correlation coefficient is

$$r = \frac{\sum(x-\overline{x})(y-\overline{y})}{\sqrt{\sum(x-\overline{x})^2 \times \sum(y-\overline{y})^2}}$$
$$\simeq \frac{33}{\sqrt{50.875 \times 26}} \simeq \frac{33}{36.3696} \simeq 0.907.$$

So, the correlation coefficient is 0.91 (rounded to two decimal places).

## Solution to Activity 11

(a) There appears to be no relationship between the two variables. Particular values for one variable do not appear to be associated with any particular values for the other variable.

(b) Ten of the points will provide positive contributions to the numerator of the correlation coefficient, whilst the other ten will provide negative contributions. So overall the positive and negative contributions will largely balance out, leading to a correlation coefficient close to zero. (In fact, the correlation coefficient is $r = +0.12$.)

## Solution to Activity 12

The pairs in 1, 3 and 5 will all have a correlation of +0.56. This is because in each case the pair of variables is the same as the original pair in the question, except for some rescaling and moving of the origin.

The pair in 2 is likely to have a different correlation as the length of a car is not just a rescaling of its weight. That is, cars with similar lengths could have very different weights.

The pair in 4 is also likely to have a different correlation, as the fuel consumption is not just a rescaling of the miles per gallon. In fact, as the miles per gallon increase, fuel consumption will decrease, so the relationship between weight and fuel consumption is likely to be negative.

## Solution to Activity 13

The relationship in (a) is clearly linear, and the relationship in (b) is clearly non-linear. So the correlation coefficient will provide a good indication about the strength of the relationship in (a) but not in (b). (In fact, although the relationships in both scatterplots look relatively strong, the correlation coefficient for (a) is $+0.98$, while that for (b) is only $+0.2$.)

In (c) and (d), the relationships do not look totally linear. However, the relationships are approximately linear. So the correlation coefficients will give approximate measures of the strength of the relationship in these two scatterplots. (It turns out that the correlation coefficient for (c) is $+0.93$, and for (d) it is $+0.95$. Both are quite close to $+1$, hence indicating strong positive relationships.)

## Solution to Activity 14

Notice that, overall, there appears to be a positive correlation between the percentage of students achieving the benchmark at Key Stage 2 in 2006 and the benchmark at Key Stage 4 in 2011.

The points representing Newport West and Monmouth appear to be influential points. With those two points on the graph, your eye follows an upwardly sloping line that goes near them and that seems in keeping with the other points. If those two points were not there though, the line your eye followed would not slope upward at all, or it would slope up only a little.

Of all the points, the point representing Islwyn is the most outlying, as it lies away from the pattern of the other points. However, it is not as remote as the points representing Newport West and Monmouth.

The various correlation coefficients are as follows.

| Points omitted | $r$ |
| --- | --- |
| None | $+0.76$ |
| Newport West | $+0.63$ |
| Newport West and Monmouth | $0.00$ |
| Islwyn | $+0.89$ |
| Islwyn, Newport West and Monmouth | $-0.42$ |

Removing the two influential points decreases the correlation from $+0.76$ to zero, whereas removing the outlier increases the magnitude of the correlation from $+0.76$ to $+0.89$. Note that removing the two influential points and the outlier has a dramatic effect on the correlation – it is then negative. However, as this means that 37.5% of the data are then not analysed, this negative correlation has little validity.

## Solution to Activity 15

No, it does not. Just because there is a positive correlation between chocolate consumption and the number of Nobel prize laureates does not mean that a country could increase its number of Nobel laureates by persuading its population to eat more chocolate, unfortunately. (This is quite apart from the issue of whether the number of Nobel prize laureates a country produces is a reasonable measure of the cleverness of its population.)

## Solution to Activity 16

(a) Letting $\mu$ denote the population mean, the hypotheses are $H_0$: $\mu = 47.0$ and $H_1$: $\mu \neq 47.0$. The test statistic is

$$z = \frac{\overline{x} - A}{s/\sqrt{n}} = \frac{50.3 - 47.0}{17.19/\sqrt{100}} \simeq 1.92.$$

This is between $-1.96$ and $1.96$, so $H_0$ is not rejected at the 5% significance level. There is little evidence that the population mean is not 47.0%.

(b) Letting $\mu$ denote the population mean, the hypotheses are $H_0$: $\mu = 53.0$ and $H_1$: $\mu \neq 53.0$. The test statistic is

$$z = \frac{50.3 - 53.0}{17.19/\sqrt{100}} \simeq -1.57.$$

This is between $-1.96$ and $1.96$, so $H_0$ is not rejected at the 5% significance level. There is little evidence that the population mean is not 53.0%.

(c) Letting $\mu$ denote the population mean, the hypotheses are $H_0$: $\mu = 55.0$ and $H_1$: $\mu \neq 55.0$. The test statistic is

$$z = \frac{50.3 - 55.0}{17.19/\sqrt{100}} \simeq -2.73.$$

This is less than $-1.96$, so $H_0$ is rejected at the 5% significance level. There is moderate evidence that the population mean is not 55.0% – in fact, it appears to be less than this.

## Solution to Activity 17

(a) $n = 50$, $\overline{x} = 15.62$ and $s = 6.44$.

We have ESE $= 6.44/\sqrt{50} \simeq 0.9108$.

A 95% confidence interval for the population mean is

$$(15.62 - 1.96 \times 0.9108, 15.62 + 1.96 \times 0.9108)$$
$$\simeq (15.62 - 1.7852, 15.62 + 1.7852)$$
$$\simeq (13.83, 17.41).$$

(b)  A 99% confidence interval for the population mean is
$$(15.62 - 2.58 \times 0.9108, 15.62 + 2.58 \times 0.9108)$$
$$\simeq (15.62 - 2.3499, 15.62 + 2.3499)$$
$$\simeq (13.27, 17.97).$$

**Solution to Activity 18**

(a)  The mean is
$$\bar{x} = \frac{\sum x}{n} = \frac{16\,946}{37} = 458.$$
The sum of the squared deviations is
$$\sum (x - \bar{x})^2 = \sum x^2 - \frac{(\sum x)^2}{n} = 7\,762\,644 - \frac{16\,946^2}{37}$$
$$\simeq 7\,762\,644 - 7\,761\,268$$
$$= 1376.$$
So the variance is
$$\frac{\sum (x - \bar{x})^2}{n - 1} \simeq \frac{1376}{36} \simeq 38.22,$$
and the standard deviation is $s \simeq \sqrt{38.22} \simeq 6.1824$.

(b)  ESE $\simeq s/\sqrt{n} = 6.1824/\sqrt{37} \simeq 1.016$.

Now
$$(\bar{x} - 1.96\,\text{ESE}, \bar{x} + 1.96\,\text{ESE})$$
$$\simeq (458 - 1.96 \times 1.016, 458 + 1.96 \times 1.016)$$
$$\simeq (458 - 1.991\,36, 458 + 1.991\,36)$$
$$\simeq (456.0, 460.0).$$

So a 95% confidence interval for the mean weight of jars of plum jam produced by this manufacturer is $(450.0\,\text{g}, 460.0\,\text{g})$.

**Solution to Activity 19**

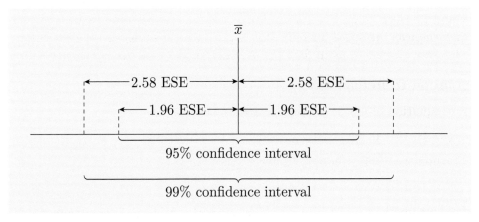

As the figure makes clear, the 99% confidence interval is always wider than the 95% confidence interval.

## Solution to Activity 20

(a) From Activity 18, the 95% confidence interval for the population mean weight is $(456.0\,\text{g}, 460.0\,\text{g})$. This interval does not contain 454, so $H_0$: $\mu = 454$ is rejected at the 5% significance level. On the basis of the confidence interval, there is moderate evidence that the mean weight is not 454 grams.

(b) The confidence interval does contain 457, so $H_0$: $\mu = 457$ is not rejected at the 5% significance level. On the basis of the confidence interval, it is plausible that the mean weight is 457 grams.

## Solution to Activity 21

From Example 13, the ESE for $\bar{x}_A - \bar{x}_B$ is 3.319, and $\bar{x}_A - \bar{x}_B = -0.9$, giving

$$(-0.9 - 1.96 \times 3.319, -0.9 + 1.96 \times 3.319)$$
$$\simeq (-0.9 - 6.51, -0.9 + 6.51)$$
$$\simeq (-7.4, 5.6).$$

So the 95% confidence interval for $\mu_A - \mu_B$ is $(-7.4\%, 5.6\%)$.

## Solution to Activity 22

The estimated standard error is

$$\text{ESE} = \sqrt{\frac{s_A^2}{n_A} + \frac{s_B^2}{n_B}} = \sqrt{\frac{18.2^2}{100} + \frac{20.6^2}{150}} \simeq 2.478.$$

Then the 95% confidence interval for $\mu_A - \mu_B$ is

$$(\bar{x}_A - \bar{x}_B - 1.96\,\text{ESE}, \bar{x}_A - \bar{x}_B + 1.96\,\text{ESE})$$
$$\simeq (58.4 - 52.1 - 1.96 \times 2.478, 58.4 - 52.1 + 1.96 \times 2.478)$$
$$\simeq (6.3 - 4.857, 6.3 + 4.857)$$
$$\simeq (1.4, 11.2).$$

The value 0 is not within this 95% confidence interval. Hence, the hypothesis that only children have the same average score as other children would be rejected at the 5% significance level. There is moderate evidence that the average score for only children is not the same for other children. The data suggest that in fact the average for only children is higher.

## Solution to Activity 23

The equation of the population least squares line is

$$y = 16.15 + 0.48x.$$

So when $x = 6$ the population mean value for $y$ is

$$y = 16.15 + 0.48 \times 6 = 19.03.$$

This means that the statement 'The interval $(18.31, 19.77)$ contains the (population) mean value of $y$ when $x = 6$' is true.

**Solution to Activity 24**

In Figure 38, seven of the 100 confidence intervals do not contain the population mean value of $y$ (including one, sample 68, which nearly contains the population mean value), and 93 of the confidence intervals do contain the population mean value. So this means that there is a 93% chance that a randomly chosen confidence interval from these 100 intervals does include the population mean value.

**Solution to Activity 25**

The confidence interval means that the statement 'The (population) mean pass rate in Mathematics is between 48.6% and 55.2% when the pass rate in English is 50%' has a 95% chance of being true.

**Solution to Activity 26**

(a) The completed table is as follows.

| Pass rate in English | Confidence interval for mean pass rate in Mathematics | Width of confidence interval |
|---|---|---|
| 40 | (40.1%, 49.3%) | 9.2% |
| 50 | (48.6%, 55.2%) | 6.6% |
| 60 | (56.9%, 61.3%) | 4.4% |
| 70 | (64.5%, 68.1%) | 3.6% |
| 80 | (71.0%, 75.9%) | 4.9% |

(b) The narrowest of the confidence intervals corresponds to a pass rate in English of 70%. A confidence interval is narrowest at the sample mean of $x$. Thus the average pass rate in English is 70% (to the nearest 10%).

**Solution to Activity 27**

Ali's prediction interval is narrower than the corresponding confidence interval, when it should be wider.

From the confidence interval for the mean response, the predicted value must be $(35.9\% + 46.4\%)/2 = 41.15\%$. However, the centre of Charlie's interval is only $(17.3\% + 55.0\%)/2 = 36.15\%$.

**Solution to Activity 28**

(a) The results at Key Stage 2 and Key Stage 4 have a positive linear relationship. This relationship appears to be reasonably strong.

(b) Yes, it is, because the relationship appears to be reasonably linear.

(c) There are no outliers. All the points seem to follow roughly the same trend.

Two points might be considered as influential, the two schools with the highest value of $P_{KS2}$. Here the performance at Key Stage 4 appears to be in line with what might be expected given the students' ability at Key Stage 2. That is, the more able a school's intake, the better those students tended to do at the end of Key Stage 4.

(d) The correlation coefficient does look reasonable. A value of +0.83 corresponds to a reasonably strong positive relationship – just like that noted in part (a).

Note that the correlation coefficient without the two potential influential points is +0.81, whereas for the full dataset it is +0.83. So, any impact of the potential influential points is small.

## Solution to Activity 29

There are 100 observations, so $n = 100$. The slope of the least squares regression line, $b$, is given by the formula

$$b = \frac{\sum(x - \bar{x})(y - \bar{y})}{\sum(x - \bar{x})^2}.$$

Now

$$\sum(x - \bar{x})^2 = \sum x^2 - \frac{(\sum x)^2}{100}$$

$$= 75\,449.44 - \frac{2743.6^2}{100}$$

$$= 75\,449.44 - 75\,273.4096 = 176.0304,$$

and

$$\sum(x - \bar{x})(y - \bar{y}) = \sum xy - \frac{(\sum x) \times (\sum y)}{100}$$

$$= 139\,903.0 - \frac{2743.6 \times 5031}{100}$$

$$= 139\,903.0 - 138\,030.516 = 1872.484.$$

So $b = 1872.484/176.0304 = 10.637$ (to three decimal places).

The intercept of the least squares regression line, $a$, is given by the formula $a = \bar{y} - b\bar{x}$.

Now,

$$\bar{x} = 2743.6/100 = 27.436 \quad \text{and} \quad \bar{y} = 5031/100 = 50.31.$$

So

$$a \simeq 50.31 - 10.637 \times 27.436$$

$$\simeq 50.31 - 291.84$$

$$= -241.53.$$

The equation of the least squares regression line is therefore $y = -241.53 + 10.637x$.

## Solution to Activity 30

(a) Between 10% and 20%.

(b) Between 55% and 60%.

(c) Between 75% and 80%.

**Solution to Activity 31**

From Activity 29,

$$\sum(x-\bar{x})^2 = 176.0304 \quad \text{and} \quad \sum(x-\bar{x})(y-\bar{y}) = 1872.484.$$

Also,

$$\sum(y-\bar{y})^2 = \sum y^2 - \frac{(\sum y)^2}{100}$$

$$= 282\,359 - \frac{5031^2}{100}$$

$$= 282\,359 - 253\,109.61 = 29\,249.39.$$

So

$$r = \frac{\sum(x-\bar{x})(y-\bar{y})}{\sqrt{\sum(x-\bar{x})^2 \times \sum(y-\bar{y})^2}}$$

$$= \frac{1872.484}{\sqrt{176.0304 \times 29\,249.39}}$$

$$\simeq \frac{1872.484}{2269.0927}$$

$$= 0.83 \text{ (rounded to two decimal places)}.$$

This is the same as the value given in Activity 28.

**Solution to Activity 32**

(a) In Activity 29 the least squares regression line was found to be

$$y = -241.53 + 10.637x,$$

where $x$ is the Key Stage 2 average points score and $y$ is the GCSE headline figure.

For School A, $x = 29.3$, so

$$y = -241.53 + 10.637 \times 29.3$$

$$\simeq -241.53 + 311.66 = 70.1 \text{ (to 1 d.p.)}.$$

For School B, $x = 28.1$, so

$$y = -241.53 + 10.637 \times 28.1$$

$$\simeq -241.53 + 298.90 = 57.4 \text{ (to 1 d.p.)}.$$

For School C, $x = 25.5$, so

$$y = -241.53 + 10.637 \times 25.5$$

$$\simeq -241.53 + 271.24 = 29.7 \text{ (to 1 d.p.)}.$$

So, in School A the predicted GCSE headline figure is 70.1%; in School B it is 57.46%; and in School C it is 29.7%.

(b) For School A, the residual is $63 - 70.1 = -7.1$.

For School B, the residual is $57 - 57.4 = -0.4$.

For School C, the residual is $51 - 29.7 = 21.3$.

In School A, the pupils did worse at the end of Key Stage 4 than is predicted by their results at Key Stage 2.

In School B, the pupils did about the same at the end of Key Stage 4 as their results at Key Stage 2 predict.

In School C, the pupils did better at the end of Key Stage 4 than is predicted by their results at Key Stage 2.

So, it appears that despite having the worst Key Stage 4 results, School C did the best job given the apparent ability of its intake. Similarly, even though School A had the best results at Key Stage 4, the school does not appear to have made the most of the potential of its students.

## Solution to Activity 33

The actual percentage of pupils in School B achieving the Key Stage 4 benchmark is well within the prediction interval given. (As the actual and predicted percentages are so close, it would be strange if this were not the case!)

In School C the actual percentage of pupils achieving the Key Stage 4 benchmark is above the prediction interval. So there is evidence that its pupils are doing distinctly better than would be expected from their performance at Key Stage 2.

## Solution to Activity 34

No, it does not. We would expect about 5% of schools to lie outside a prediction interval – that is, about five of the 100 schools plotted. So having six schools lying outside the prediction interval in Figure 43 is not much more that we would expect if the model is correct.

## Solution to Activity 35

If we are not taking the Key Stage 2 results into account, then just the schools at the top of the plot (high $P_{KS4}$) will be classified as good, and the schools towards the bottom of the plot (low $P_{KS4}$) classified as bad.

One of the two schools that lie below the 95% prediction interval has a value of $P_{KS4}$ that is sufficiently low that it might still be judged as bad on the basis of just its Key Stage 4 results.

The other five schools that lie outside the 95% prediction interval do not have a value of $P_{KS4}$ that is noticeably either high or low. So, when the Key Stage 2 results are ignored, these schools will not be picked out as noticeably good or bad. This means, in particular, that the schools that performed well, given the ability of their intake, no longer stand out.

# Solutions to exercises

### Solution to Exercise 1

Factors 1 and 3 could both be tested using a two-sample $z$-test. This is because these factors split the schools into two groups (sixth form or no sixth form; allows early GCSEs or does not allow early GCSEs). The mean $P_{KS4}$ could be calculated for each group, and the two means could then be compared in a hypothesis test.

The other two factors (size of school and proportion eligible for free schools meals) would have to be split into two groups before a two-sample $z$-test could be used. Such a split is likely to be arbitrary, making it difficult to interpret the results from the test.

### Solution to Exercise 2

From strongest to weakest the order of the correlations is as follows.

$$-0.99 \quad +0.80 \quad -0.30 \quad +0.25 \quad +0.04$$

This is because the correlation gets weaker as the coefficient gets closer to zero. The sign of the correlation coefficient is unimportant.

### Solution to Exercise 3

The correlation coefficient turns out to be $+0.74$. Correlation coefficients are hard to estimate accurately, so a reasonable guess would be somewhere between $+0.50$ and $+0.95$.

### Solution to Exercise 4

The five initial sums that are required are as follows:

$$\sum x = 184.89, \quad \sum y = 92.06,$$
$$\sum x^2 = 3798.2743, \quad \sum y^2 = 941.7382, \quad \sum xy = 1891.2141.$$

As $n = 9$,

$$\sum (x - \overline{x})^2 = 3798.2743 - \frac{184.89^2}{9} = 3798.2743 - 3798.2569$$
$$= 0.0174,$$

$$\sum (y - \overline{y})^2 = 941.7382 - \frac{92.06^2}{9}$$
$$\simeq 941.7382 - 941.6715 \text{ (rounded to four decimal places)}$$
$$= 0.0667,$$

and

$$\sum (x - \overline{x})(y - \overline{y}) = 1891.2141 - \frac{184.89 \times 92.06}{9}$$
$$\simeq 1891.2141 - 1891.2193 \text{ (rounded to four decimal places)}$$
$$= -0.0052.$$

We can now calculate the correlation coefficient.

$$r = \frac{\sum(x - \overline{x})(y - \overline{y})}{\sqrt{\sum(x - \overline{x})^2 \sum(x - \overline{x})^2}}$$

$$\simeq \frac{-0.0052}{\sqrt{0.0174 \times 0.0667}} \simeq -0.15 \text{ (rounded to two decimal places)}.$$

Note that this correlation coefficient is considerably different from the correlation coefficient based on 100 sprinters. One explanation for this is that it is based on a relatively small sample, and a fairly biased one at that, as it consists of the best nine 200-metre sprinters.

## Solution to Exercise 5

(a) There appears to be a positive relationship between the two variables. High values for one variable appear to be associated with high values for the other variable. Also, low values for one variable appear to be associated with low values for the other variable.

(b) Most of the points will provide positive contributions to the numerator of the correlation coefficient. Only three of the points will provide negative contributions to the correlation coefficient (and quite small contributions at that, as they are close to $(\overline{x}, \overline{y})$). So overall the correlation coefficient is going to be positive. (In fact the correlation coefficient is $r = +0.90$.)

## Solution to Exercise 6

(a) No, the correlation coefficient would not change. It does not matter which variable is labelled as $x$.

(b) No, the correlation coefficient would not change. Adding a constant to a variable does not change a correlation coefficient.

(c) No, the correlation coefficient still would not change. Multiplying by a constant does not change a correlation coefficient, nor does adding a constant. Hence doing one followed by the other does not change it.

## Solution to Exercise 7

The point representing Harry Aikines-Aryeety appears to be an outlier. His times lie away from the general pattern of the other points for both the 100 metres and the 200 metres. The point representing Leon Baptiste belongs to the general pattern. However, with a time of more than 10.40 seconds for the 100 metres, his time is noticeably slower than the other sprinters in this elite group. So the point representing Leon Baptiste might be counted as an influential point. If his point is removed, the correlation changes sign!

The various correlation coefficients are as follows.

| Points omitted | $r$ |
|---|---|
| None | −0.15 |
| Harry Aikines-Aryeety | −0.62 |
| Leon Baptiste | +0.10 |
| Harry Aikines-Aryeety and Leon Baptiste | −0.46 |

Removing the outlier increases the magnitude of the correlation coefficient from 0.15 to 0.62, whereas removing the influential point decreases the magnitude to 0.10.

### Solution to Exercise 8

(a) On the plot, the point representing pineapples appears to be to be an outlier. It is rated as being relatively tasty but very difficult. This is at odds with the positive correlation between tastiness and easiness implied by the positioning of the other fruits on the plot. (Fruits that are relatively easy are also seen as relatively tasty.)

There do not appear to be any influential points. None of the fruits are unusually tasty, unusually untasty, unusually difficult or unusually easy.

(b) No, the conclusion is not appropriate. Although easy to eat fruits also tend to be the ones that are tasty, this does not mean that being easy to eat *causes* a fruit to be tasty. (Nor does being tasty cause a fruit to be rated as being easy to eat.)

### Solution to Exercise 9

(a)    $\text{ESE} = s/\sqrt{n} = 5.1/\sqrt{30} \simeq 0.931$.

Thus, a 95% confidence interval for the mean skull breadth (in millimetres) in that period is

$$(\bar{x} - 1.96\,\text{ESE}, \bar{x} + 1.96\,\text{ESE})$$
$$\simeq (131.4 - 1.96 \times 0.931, 131.4 + 1.96 \times 0.931)$$
$$\simeq (131.4 - 1.825, 131.4 + 1.825)$$
$$\simeq (129.6, 133.2).$$

(b) The 99% confidence interval would be wider. This is because a 99% confidence interval is always wider than the 95% confidence interval.

### Solution to Exercise 10

The estimated standard error is

$$\text{ESE} = \sqrt{\frac{3.4^2}{30} + \frac{5.1^2}{30}} \simeq 1.119.$$

Thus the 95% confidence interval for the change in mean skull breadth (in mm) from 4000 BC to 1850 BC is

$$(134.5 - 131.4 - 1.96 \times 1.119, 134.5 - 131.4 + 1.96 \times 1.119)$$
$$\simeq (3.1 - 2.193, 3.1 + 2.193)$$
$$\simeq (0.9, 5.3).$$

As 0 mm is not in the 95% confidence interval, there is reasonably strong evidence that the mean skull breadth changed between 4000 BC and 1850 BC. With 95% confidence, the mean breadth increased by between 0.9 mm and 5.3 mm during this time.

## Solution to Exercise 11

(a) When $x = 110$,

$$y = 4.2 + 0.880 \times 110 = 4.2 + 96.8 = 101.0.$$

So for patients with an initial diastolic blood pressure of $110\,\text{mmHg}$, the predicted post-injection blood pressure is $101.0\,\text{mmHg}$.

This estimate does not give any information about the uncertainty in the estimate. This information is important if the estimate is going to be used to make decisions.

(b) Yes, it does. This is because there is a high chance that it is correct to say that the mean post-injection diastolic blood pressure is in the range $95.9\,\text{mmHg}$ to $106.1\,\text{mmHg}$ – values that are all lower than the initial diastolic blood pressure.

(c) No, it does not. The confidence interval provides information about the uncertainty of the estimate for the population mean – not that of individuals. For that, a prediction interval is required.

In fact, the prediction interval is $81.2\,\text{mmHg}$ to $120.8\,\text{mmHg}$. This interval includes values above $110\,\text{mmHg}$, which means that for any individual patient, their diastolic blood pressure might actually go up after treatment with captopril, not down.

## Solution to Exercise 12

(a) There is a 95% chance that the statement 'the sprinter's best time for the 100-metre sprint in 2011 would have been between 9.88 seconds and 10.62 seconds' is true.

(b) The point estimate is always in the middle of the prediction interval. As $(9.88 + 10.62)/2 = 10.25$, the point estimate must have been 10.25 seconds.

(c) Yes, it is plausible, because the B qualifying time is within the range of times given by the 95% prediction interval.

(d) Yes, they do. Seven of the points lie outside of the 95% prediction intervals. This is not much more than the five that would be expected.

## Solution to Exercise 13

(a) From Activity 29 we had that

$$P_{\text{KS4}} = -241.53 + 10.637 P_{\text{KS2}}.$$

So when $P_{\text{KS2}} = 31.0$, the predicted value of $P_{\text{KS4}}$ is

$$-241.53 + 10.637 \times 31.0 = 88.2 \text{ (to 1 d.p.)}.$$

Thus for a school where $P_{\text{KS2}} = 31.0$, it is predicted that 88.2% of its students finish Key Stage 4 with at least five A* to C grade GCSEs including English and Mathematics.

(b) Consider the statement 'The (population) average of $P_{KS4}$ for schools where at intake $P_{KS2} = 31.0$ is between 82.7% and 93.8%.' This confidence interval means that there is a 95% chance that this statement is true.

Note that this interval refers to the average of $P_{KS4}$ for all such schools, and not the value of $P_{KS4}$ for any single school.

(c) No, they do not. It is not possible to get more that 100% of students passing at least five A* to C grade GSCEs including English and Mathematics. So the maximum possible value of $P_{KS4}$ is 100%. This is less than the predicted value. Also, most of the range quoted for the prediction interval is above 100%.

## Solution to Exercise 14

(a) Let $y$ represent $P_{KS4}$, and $x$ represent $P_{KS2}$. From Table 11:

$$\sum x = 483.9, \quad \sum y = 1473,$$
$$\sum x^2 = 15\,620.91, \quad \sum y^2 = 144\,747, \quad \sum xy = 47\,543.7.$$

So

$$\sum (x - \bar{x})^2 = 15\,620.91 - 483.9^2/15 = 10.296,$$
$$\sum (y - \bar{y})^2 = 144\,747 - 1473^2/15 = 98.4,$$
$$\sum (x - \bar{x})(y - \bar{y}) = 47\,543.7 - (483.9 \times 1473)/15 = 24.72.$$

So, the correlation coefficient, $r$, is as follows.

$$r = \frac{\sum (x - \bar{x})(y - \bar{y})}{\sqrt{\sum (x - \bar{x})^2 \times \sum (y - \bar{y})^2}}$$
$$= \frac{24.72}{\sqrt{10.296 \times 98.4}} \simeq 0.78.$$

(b) There is some suggestion that the relationship between $P_{KS2}$ and $P_{KS4}$ is non-linear because $P_{KS4}$ has to level out at 100 or below. So the correlation coefficient probably underestimates the strength of the relationship between $P_{KS2}$ and $P_{KS4}$.

# Acknowledgements

Grateful acknowledgement is made to the following sources:

Figure 31 Taken from: www.bbc.co.uk/news/magazine-20356613

Figure 32 Adapted from: www.topsinathletics.info

Subsection 1.1 cartoon at end (Beagle Elementary School), Rod Maclean / www.justkiddingcartoons.com

Subsection 1.1 photo (GCSE certificate), www.slideshare.net/Muppet1971/gcse-english-summer-1989

Subsection 1.2 photo (SATS papers), taken from: www.sats-past-papers.co.uk/images/S8300645.jpg

Subsection 2.2 cartoon ('Correlation Street'), www.cartoonstock.com

Exercises on Section 2, photo (Marlon Devonish) © MaxiSports / www.dreamstime.com

Subsection 3.4 cartoon (causation): Jyrinx/www.flickr.com/photos/26353267@N03/4026814703. This file is licensed under the Creative Commons Attribution-Non-commercial Licence http://creativecommons.org/licenses/by-nc/3.0/

Exercises on Section 3, figure (tastiness of fruit), www.causeweb.org

Subsection 4.2 photo (child writing): With Permission: Heather Whitaker

Subsection 4.2 photo (jam), AVRORRA / www.istockphoto.com

Subsection 4.3 photo (family) © imtmphoto / www.istockphoto.com

Exercises on Section 4, photo (Egyptian mask), taken from: www.touregypt.net/featurestories/masks.htm

Subsection 5.1 photo (Scrooge), taken from: www.stjohnec.org/portfolio/a-christmas-carol-class-of-2013-adrianne-as-scrooge

Exercises on Section 5, cartoon (sprinters), www.cartoonstock.com

Section 6 cartoon (decent school), www.cartoonstock.com

Every effort has been made to contact copyright holders. If any have been inadvertently overlooked the publishers will be pleased to make the necessary arrangements at the first opportunity.

# Index